THE FORTEAN TIMES BOOK OF
MEDICAL MAYHEM

THE FORTEAN TIMES BOOK OF
MEDICAL MAYHEM

COMPILED BY
IAN SIMMONS, PAUL SIEVEKING
& VAL STEVENSON
ILLUSTRATIONS BY ED TRAQUINO

JOHN BROWN PUBLISHING

First published in Great Britain in August 1999
by John Brown Publishing Ltd, The New Boathouse,
Bramley Road, London W10 6SR, UK.
Tel 0171 565 3000. Fax 0171 565 3050.

First impression August 1999

ISBN 1 902212 193

Printed and bound in Great Britain by
Creative Print and Design (Wales) Ebbw Vale, Gwent

CONTENTS

Medical matters seem to loom large in public life and interest. You just need to take a look at the TV schedules to see that. Ever since *Emergency Ward 10* nearly 40 years ago, there's been some sort of medical drama near the top of the ratings, and for many people their prime topic of conversation seems to be their latest operation, injury or plague of boils, going on to an evaluation of the overall health of family, friends and neighbourhood. Yes, it could be said that the British have an obsession with the medical. Of course, being ill or going into hospital is no fun. Viewed from a distance, health matters are, on the one hand, macabrely fascinating and sometimes scary, and, on the other, often deeply weird or downright hilarious, as we hope to show in the following pages.

I doubt that *Casualty* will ever run a storyline about people growing horns, having three eyes or undergoing a brain operation with a rusty hand drill. Nor will *ER* feature exploding stomach contents, mysterious hill walker deaths, or someone charged for group therapy with their multiple personalities (including Satan, angels who talked to God, and a duck), but you will find all these mind-wrenching tales in here, along with many many more which will amuse, amaze and inform.

Many of these tales have appeared in the pages of the *Fortean Times* over the years, but a whole load more are drawn from our vast files containing all the great stories we just haven't had room to get into the mag. Whether all these stories are true, is hard to say, and much as we'd like to, we just don't have the resources to check up on every tale we print. What is certain is that all of these stories have appeared somewhere in the world's press as true at some time, and at the back of the book you'll find the list of references which will allow you to judge for yourself the reliability of our sources. Even the most reputable papers are not above running the occasional urban legend as fact, or recycling old human interest stories as space fillers, perhaps with a name or location altered. Where we do think a story is a little suspect, we've tried to make our suspicions known.

Of course, this book would not have happened without the vast legion of forteans worldwide who take the trouble to scour their local papers for strange tales, clip them for us, send them to Fortean Towers or post them on the fortean mailing list on the Internet. They certainly share the British fascination with all things medical. Without their dedication there would be no *Fortean Times* and no books like this. Keep it up!

IAN SIMMONS & PAUL SIEVEKING

LITTLE BIG

In any average population, there are going to be some
people who tend towards the extremes.

ZACK STREKERT looks like a miniature Sumo wrestler.
At 17 months, he weighed almost 68lb, as much as an nine-
year-old. He was 3ft tall and nearly as big around. His ankles
wouldn't fit into shoes, and on hot days he wore nothing but a
nappy in the largest adult size. No evidence of a glandular disorder was found. The diagnosis was 'morbid obesity', but his
mother Laurie, 29, said he had never been a big eater: "He'll
have a quarter cup of cereal for breakfast, crackers for a snack,
and half a sandwich for lunch." He weighed a mere 10lb 12oz
at birth. Zack is a celebrity in the small town of Goshen, near
Bloomingburg, 60 miles north of New York City. Being big
runs in the family. Zack's mother is 5ft 10in and 220lb and her
husband Chris 6ft 3in. Her son Andrew, seven, from a previous marriage, weighs 121lb, twice the average. Only four-year-
old Summer is slender.

CHAPTER ONE

ETHAN GILBY was born in March after a 19-hour labour in Grimsby Maternity Hospital. He weighed 12lb 4oz, almost double the average, and within a year grew to 32lb, with no signs of slowing down. The average weight at one year is 20lb. The infant Hercules was nearly 3ft tall and had broader shoulders than his sister Naomi, four. His mother Shellie, 22, of Cleethorpes, south Humberside, dressed him in clothes for three-year-olds. He was introduced to solid food at six weeks and his favourite meal is now smoked fish and potatoes. "He's unbelievably strong," she said. His size was caused by a hormonal disorder of the adrenal gland, a bit like being on anabolic steroids from birth – hence his great strength. "He can lift the video recorder and push his high chair across the room." His size came as a surprise – Mrs Gilby is slender and only 5ft 2in tall, while her husband Phil is of average height. Another one-year-old, Jordan Palmer from Cadbourne, Lincolnshire, is the same size and weight as Ethan, and Shannon Fox weighed 35lb in February when she was only 11 months old. The heaviest baby of the century was born in Italy in 1955 and weighed 22lb. Guy Warwick Carr, the heaviest baby born in the UK this century, weighed 15lb 8oz at birth in 1992.

THOMAS HIORNS, at the age of four, could already lift three times his own body-weight, kick a ball the full length of a football pitch and scale high walls in seconds. He weighed nearly four stone and was as tall as the average 10-year-old. His superhuman strength results from the rarest genetic disorder known: he is the only person in the world with 49 chromosomes instead of 46. His father Jimmy fought in Desert Storm, and it is thought Thomas's strange disorder could be a result of Gulf War Syndrome.

EXCESSIVE MERCURY in the drinking water of Huilong village in central Sichuan province, China, has been identified as the reason why about 60 villagers are dwarves, according to the Xinhua news agency. No new cases of dwarfism were reported after the village was assured a supply of pollution-free drinking water. The report did not say when the clean water was provided. Mercury is not known to produce dwarfism, and it is odd that the villagers did not apparently suffer from any of the known toxic effects of mercury.

GUL MOHAMMED, at 22.5in the shortest man in the world, died at the age of 40. He was a familiar figure in the fœtid alleys of old Delhi, where he felt at home among the beggars, eunuchs and saddhus of this largely Muslim quarter of town. He was too short to leap across the open sewers and gullies, and was carried across these obstacles by whoever was at hand. He chain-smoked all his life and died in hospital after a long struggle with asthma and bronchitis. He was born on 15 February 1957; his twin brother Zahoor died when he was four. Gul (flower in Urdu) never overcame a lifelong dislike of children, who mocked and bullied him, forcing him to give up school and begin scratching a living selling sweetmeats. Children often stole from him, but they were too fast to catch and too big to reprimand. He often talked to the eunuchs about his dreams – such as marrying a tall actress – because they never laughed at him.

AFTER Gul Mohammed's death, his title was passed to Younis Edwan, 27, a 25.6in (65cm) tall Jordanian. Mr Edwan, who lives in Amman, yearns for a 'normal life' and an 'understanding wife'. He complains that people don't treat him like an adult and that he is often ridiculed. Officials from the *Guinness Book of Records* say they need an average of measurements at different times of day to register his official height; they had no record of anyone shorter at the present time. Another contender is Mohammed Rana, 26, from Bangladesh, but at 2ft 5in, he is clearly not the winner. One of the contenders for shortest woman in the world is Myrna Graham, 43, from St Elizabeth in Jamaica, who is 29in tall and has a son of 14, who is twice her size.

HAJI MOHAMMED ALAM CHANNA, 42, said to be the world's tallest man, died in New York in July 1998 from kidney failure. He was also said to hold the record for the world's biggest feet (size 22). He was born in Pakistan's southern Sindh province and grew until he was 28. He reached 7ft 7in, according to the *Guinness Book of Records*, though he claimed he was 7ft 8in. An AP report, however, said the tallest man in the world – at 7ft 8in – was Ri Myong-hun, of North Korea. Orphaned at the age of five, Alam Channa had only a few years of schooling before starting work in the fields. His height made him a minor celebrity and he travelled the world as 'Pakistan's mobile ambassador'. He was unable to stand for years. An over-active pituitary gland produced the growth hormone which made him into a giant, but also inhibited production of insulin; and complications from diabetes led to kidney and bladder problems, and damaged the nerves in his legs and spine. He had only one functioning kidney. He blamed the start of his troubles on a bad car accident in 1988, and in 1995 another crash exacerbated his back problems. "Before I became ill I was very happy, but now I just wish I had been normal," he said. After August 1997, his 400lb frame was confined to two hospital beds joined end-to-end in a windowless basement room of Islamabad's Shifa hospital, and he had four constant attendants and companions. Local doctors argued they could reconstruct his bladder and perform other surgery to ease his pain, but his supporters were adamant he be treated in the US at government expense. Eventually, prime minister Nawaz Sharif ordered Channa to be sent abroad. He went into a coma in New York's Westchester County Medical Center in June and was unable to travel to Houston, where he was to have treatment. He is survived by his wife, Nasim, and an eight-year-old son, Abid Ali, who is of normal height.

THERE IS CLEARLY much confusion in this area. John Paul Ofwono, 30, from the village of Yokolo in eastern Uganda, who is claimed to be 8ft 2in tall and can pick mangoes without climbing trees, is also said to be the world's tallest. During the Holy Spirit Movement insurgency, led by the spirit medium Alice Lakwena in eastern Uganda in the mid-1980s, Ofwono frightened well-armed government soldiers, who took him for the ghost spirit of Lakwena. Ofwono, who weighs 322lb, towers over his father, who is quite short – 5ft 5in. The giant sees his stature as a burden: he dropped out of primary school after being teased by other children, has been shunned by the women of his village and is in poor health. He has not travelled more than a few miles from his home village; one problem is that he cannot fit into a car. Another claimant to be the world's tallest man – Rajan Adhikary of Sharnamati village in the Jhapa district of Nepal – is only 7ft 9in, which still makes him taller than Channa and Myong hun

THE TALLEST MAN of whom there is irrefutable evidence was the American Robert Pershing Wadlow (1918–40). Two weeks before his death, he was 8ft 11.1in tall. He was still growing and would probably have topped 9ft had he survived for another year. The tallest recorded 'true' (non-pathological) giant was Angus Macaskill (1823–63), born on the island of Berneray in Scotland, who stood at 7ft 9in.

BUILDERS in Brooklyn removed a bay window and several rows of bricks so that a 1,000lb man could be taken to hospital to save his life. Michael Hebranko, 43, who put on hundreds of extra pounds in the months after he lost control of his eating addiction, was critically ill with heart and respiratory problems, and gangrene. He is possibly the heaviest person alive, but is way under the official record of 1,400lb held by the late John Brower Minnoch of Bainbridge Island, Washington. For nine weeks, Hebranko was unable to stand for more than 30 seconds and was confined to a sofa in his living room, covered in a blanket because no clothes fitted his 110in waist. A team of 20 paramedics lifted him through the 10ft-by-5ft hole in the wall on a special stretcher designed to transport small whales, after which he was loaded into the ambulance with a fork-lift truck. Mr Hebranko, who lives with his wife and 19-year-old son, dropped from 904lb to a mere 199lb in 1989 and his photograph was used to advertise diet guru Richard Simmons's Deal-a-Meal programme; but in 1994 he lapsed and began to gain more weight than ever.

THE LARGEST ovarian cyst ever recorded weighed 328lb and was drained and removed in Texas in 1905. The largest ever removed intact weighed 303lb. This was from a 34-year-old woman in Stanford, California, in 1991.

BIRTHS

For some, the strangeness begins the moment they arrive
in the world – or even before

FROM the *Montgomery Advertiser,* Alabama: "Infertility
unlikely to be passed on."

A MOTHER gave birth to twins, one black and one white.
Michelle Hamilton, 31, has a black father and a white mother
and the twins' father, Robert Calvert, is black. The babies were
delivered by Cæsarean section on 27 June, a month premature, at St George's Hospital, Tooting, south London. Jolene,
who is white, weighed 5lb 2oz and Robert Jr, who is black, 4lb
6oz. "One of my other daughters was born white, but has
grown darker," said Ms Hamilton, who has four older children
and lives in Wandsworth. In China, a Chinese couple confused doctors by giving birth to a black baby. According to the
Zhuhai Special Zone Daily, the child was "black as ink". There
was nothing special about the newborn child, but a month
later he began to turn black, ending up totally black except for

reddish hair, and yellow palms and feet, making him a "yellow person with black skin" according to the paper.

IN BEIJING, doctors were also baffled, this time by a pregnant woman who claimed she was being kept awake at night by the crying of her unborn child. The 27-year-old said she thought she was dreaming when she heard a baby crying "in her left ear" while asleep, but when her husband pressed his ear against hers, he could also hear the sound. Hospital doctors could also hear the crying, but when they scanned the fœtus, it was shown to have its mouth closed when the sounds were being made.

PAULINE STONE, 37, who runs the Vittoria pub in Clifton, Bristol, flew to Cuba for a second honeymoon with her husband Philip three days after she discovered she was pregnant. She thought she had been carrying the baby for only a few weeks, as she had not put on much weight. Two days later, she gave birth to Margaret, a 4lb 6oz baby girl. Margaret is thought to be the first Briton born in Cuba since Castro took power in 1959.

A BRAZILIAN widow who complained of slight stomach pains discovered she was carrying the skeleton of a 20in (51cm) fœtus conceived outside her womb at least 15 years earlier. An X-ray taken at the Hospital das Clinicas, in the north-eastern city of Recife, showed that Antonieta Hilario dos Prazeres, 62, carried the perfectly formed skeleton in an area close to her stomach. She had gone through the menopause 10 years earlier and had not had sexual relations for 15 years. "This is an extremely rare case," said the obstetrician Edmundo Macedo Ferraz. Six months later, on 3 October, another Brazilian woman had surgery in Campo Grande, west of Rio de Janeiro, to remove a mummified ectopic fœtus lodged in her body for 22 years. Wanda Maria da Conceicao, 52, had known all along that the fœtus was there, but had decided to leave it alone until it started to cause her some pain. The mother of five made a good recovery in hospital.

NATASHA TILSLEY, 18, of Lanner in Cornwall, had the surprise of her life when she gave birth to a baby girl after drinking a glass of liver salts: she thought she was constipated. In a state of shock, she wrapped the baby in a towel and put her in the garden shed with a torch left on. Her father found the crying baby the next day. The night before the birth she had worked as a waitress until midnight, and six weeks earlier she had been modelling swimsuits. She remained a size eight right up to the birth.

HUMAN PLACENTA cookery is no longer just a hippie health fad; there is an increasingly widespread belief that eating the placenta can ward off post-natal depression. "I'd describe the taste as gamey," said Jane, the wife of Greg, a stockbroker. "I think the biggest mistake Greg made first time around was putting it into the freezer whole. He got through three hacksaw blades trying to cut off a bit each day." They did not repeat the mistake when their second daughter was born. Freezer bag at the ready, Greg took home the placenta ("half the size of a rugby ball"), but this time he immediately cut it up into individual oven-ready portions, which he froze and served up to his wife over eight days with pasta or salad on the side. Here's one recipe given by Kate Berridge in *Esquire* magazine: "Anthony Worrell Thompson's Crostini of Placenta with Vin Santo: Cook with olive oil, onion, Vin Santo, capers and anchovies. Blend in a food processor and spread on toasted crostini. The perfect canapé for a christening party."

FOUR REGULARS at the Star Inn, Outwood, West Yorkshire, fathered triplets – all two boys and a girl – in four years. Newsagent Marcus Jones, 34, was the first. His wife Ruth gave birth to Charlie, Stephanie and Oliver. Then it was Adrian Jeffery, 38, a bathroom company manager, whose wife Jill produced Ben, Victoria and Sam. Six weeks later, Ryan, Benjamin and Jessica arrived to delighted recreation officer Amma Sohal, 30, and his wife Linda. Finally, in 1996, Graham Anderson, 35, general manager of a chain of plant nurseries, and his wife Lorraine, announced the arrival of George, Laura and Harry. Lorraine is the daughter of the Star Inn's publican, Ivor Lloyd, who said: "It must be something in the beer."

TWO SISTERS gave birth at exactly the same time at Darlington Memorial Hospital. Tracy Harrison, 27, had James, weighing 7lb 3oz as Vicky, 19, produced Chlöe, 6lb 12oz. They planned a synchronised christening.

TWO SETS of American quadruplets were born on succeeding days in April at the University Hospital in Iowa City, the same hospital where septuplets, one of three sets born alive in recent times, were born to Bobbie and Kenny McCaughey in November 1998. The McCaugheys, from Des Moines, turned down millions of dollars for their story, but settled in the end for a TV programme on which they aired their religious views. Kimberley Grady and her husband Daniel's four daughters were delivered on 1 April 1998, 14 weeks early. Ashley Irene weighed 1lb 15oz; Lindsey Lucille, 1lb 12oz; Kara Colleen, 1lb 11oz; and Alyssa Anne, 1lb 9oz. The following day, Mike and Jody Eastridge had one boy and three girls, born eight weeks early. Katie weighed 3lb 9oz; Emily, 4lb 2oz; Amanda, 4lb 3oz; and Chad, 5lb 6oz. The McCaughey septuplets and the Eastridge quads were conceived through *in vitro* fertilisation, but the Grady quads were conceived without such treatment, a much rarer event.

ANOTHER SET of surviving septuplets was born on 14 January, 1998, to Hasna Mohammed Humair, a Saudi woman of 40 who already had six children. The four boys and three girls were delivered in the Abha obstetric hospital in Aseer, 750 miles south of Riyadh. The unplanned pregnancy occurred while the mother was taking a fertility drug to regulate her menstrual cycle, and the babies were born eight weeks premature. A month later, all seven were in good health and their weight increase had been between 2.5lb and 3lb. The initial news report quoted the father, Abdullah Mohammed Ali, a semi-retired taxi driver aged 55, as saying: "We're ecstatic and can't wait for them to join their brothers and sisters at home", but on 1 March, Hind Moussa, a pædiatrician at the hospital, threatened to call the police unless the parents took the seven-week-old babies home. The nursery was overcrowded and the staff were running out of patience. Mrs Humair asked for more time, pleading chronic fatigue. Three months after their birth, the babies were still at the hospital. The couple had separated as the result of all the publicity, and Mrs Humair had been disowned by her own parents because local television had showed a picture of her unveiled. In mid-April, Saudi Crown Prince Abdullah donated 200,000 riyals (£32,000) to help.

CRISTINA HERNANDEZ gave birth to three boys and three girls in Mexico City three months before term. Doctors had earlier caused a sensation by announcing that Hernandez, 28, already a mother of a 10-year-old girl, was carrying up to nine fœtuses. The six babies were put in incubators, but were said to be in good health. It was not stated whether Hernandez had taken fertility drugs.

CHAPTER TWO

DISCOUNTING dubious accounts of up to 15 children born together, the official record for multiple births remains nine. Nontuplets – five boys and four girls – were born to Geraldine Bridrick in Sydney on 13 June 1971; none survived beyond six days. Quindecaplets, the fœtuses of 10 girls and five boys, were reportedly aborted from the womb of a 35-year-old woman who was four months pregnant after fertility treatment, by Dr Gennaro Montanino in Rome in July 1971.

LEONTINA ALBINA (née Espinoza), a Chilean listed in the *Guinness Book of Records* as the most prolific living mother, died aged 73 on 6 August at her home in San Antonio, Chile, after succumbing to a diabetic coma. Between 1943 and 1981, she had given birth to 55 (or 57) children, including nine sets of triplets and 11 pairs of twins. Only 40 (24 boys and 16 girls) survived her. The record is held by the wife of 18th century Russian peasant Feodor Vassilyev, who had 69 children.

61 YEARS after he was born, Jerry Henricksen, a businessman from Spokane, Washington, finally paid the hospital bill for his own birth in 1935. Mr Henricksen was sorting through his mother's papers after her death when he came across the unpaid bill, so he went to St Mary's Hospital in Pierre, South Dakota where he had been born and settled up the debt, $70, plus 61-years' interest – a total of $238.30.

CURIOUS CURES

Whatever medical science can achieve, there are always cures which come as a complete surprise – but don't try these at home!

CAR CLEANER Layton Brewer, 22, blind in one eye for three years after being struck by a mystery virus, was cured when he accidentally squirted caustic cleaning fluid into his eye. "Our only explanation for what's happened is that it's a remarkable coincidence," said a spokesman at Southampton Eye Hospital. Then again, perhaps not. Blind pensioner Ben Sturnham regained his sight by accidentally spraying furniture polish in his eyes. "I was polishing the sideboard when I got the can the wrong way round and sprayed it into my eyes," he said. "I sat down feeling a bit shaky and wiped it out with a tissue. When the stinging stopped I opened my eyes and realised I could see right across the street." Doctors were also at a loss.

AN ODD (and possibly apocryphal) case was reported in May 1995: blind Indian Gauri Banerjee, 64, knocked his head against a door and regained his sight after 20 years. And lost his hearing. In Exmouth, Devon, Christopher Holcombe, 50, had been blind for five years when he collapsed unconscious in his flat. Several days later, he awoke from his coma to find he could see again, but had lost his memory. "I am a little confused," he said. "I don't recall being blind, I hope I will be able to recall my life and get on with it." Elsewhere, Canadian Bob Aubrey got his sight back when he tripped over his guide dog, and Pedro Alvarez of Santiago, Chile, confused doctors by getting his sight back after having one of his teeth pulled.

LEE MILLER from Doncaster, a private in the Territorial Army, was bitten on the head by a bot-fly during a 10-week adventure holiday in Belize. A larva grew underneath his scalp, and six weeks later he was in Sheffield's Royal Hallamshire Hospital, where doctors attempted to lure the white maggot out by bandaging his scalp with bacon rashers for 30 hours. Consultant Michael McKendrick explained that the bacon starved the larva of oxygen and tempted it to come out for a snack. "Vaseline and animal fat have been tried in the past," he said, "but it is the fatty content of bacon which seems to work." Presumably, the treatment was successful.

ON 8 JUNE, 1997, more than 300,000 people with respiratory ailments converged on a small house in Hyderabad, India, for a miracle cure of herbs and water stuffed inside a live fish. The Goud/Bathini family, which has been giving away the medicine for 152 years, started distributing it at 5am, during the auspicious Mrigasira solar phase, which occurs once a year for two days. Indian railways ran three special trains to bring patients from all over India, while Indian Airlines flew an 'asthma special' from New Delhi. Patients pay about 8p for a 2in murrel fish and swallow it live after the Gouds have stuffed their secret herbal mixture in its mouth. People who have taken the cure say the fish helps to clear the food pipe as it makes its way down to the stomach, and later releases the medicine. It survives for about 15 minutes, clearing accumulated phlegm as it flaps about. Patients are advised to begin a strict 45-day diet, and to abstain from alcohol, caffeine, tobacco, and deep-fried foods. They must repeat the treatment at least two years in a row. According to legend, a Himalayan saint revealed the wonder cure to Bathini Veeranna Goud in 1845. "I don't know how it works. Perhaps it's God's blessing," said Harinath Goud, one of the five brothers who know the formula. They refuse to divulge the secret, even to medical researchers, for fear it will be used for profit. The saint had warned that the remedy would lose its potency if it were commercialised. The family, 250 members of which distributed the cure from 25 counters, said they expected half a million patients, and had prepared about 90lb of medicine. They had pooled money earned as landlords, farmers and office workers to raise the £650 needed to buy the necessary ingredients. Harinath Goud claims 90 per cent of the patients are cured, but offers no evidence. As a child, he saw people come in the tens of thousands to swallow fish more than 40 years ago. Word spread and the numbers steadily grew.

DARREN GARSIDE, 15, touched a mains electricity cable while rescuing four-year-old Jay Nother from a hole dug by workmen. He was thrown 9ft (2.7m) through the air and suffered severe burns to his face, left arm and back; his life was saved by the thick rubber soles on his trainers. After being released from Salisbury District Hospital, he found that his acne was cured. "I used to have spots all over my face," he said. "Now the skin has peeled off and they've gone."

WHEN he saw his father drown during a fishing trip, nine-year-old Jon Pasko lost the ability to speak. He finally broke his silence 24 years later when he fell out of a boat in Sorrento, Italy, and yelled for help.

MURRAY ATWELL, a club doorman from Dunster, Somerset, lost his lifelong stammer when his four-year-old son Connery accidentally banged his head with a 'hockey stick' broom handle. The blow knocked him flat and made him dizzy. As his wife was away, he didn't notice that his stammer had gone until the next day when he chatted to his mother.

A JUDGE in Perugia, central Italy, dismissed fraud charges against Moerno Bracci, 29, employed as a telephonist under a state programme to help the blind, who was spotted driving to work. He had lost his sight in a road crash five years earlier, but claimed to have regained it miraculously at the shrine of Lourdes on 13 December, the feast day of St Lucia, patron saint of the blind.

LAWYER Mary Dignan was hit by a train and knocked unconscious as she hurried to a hearing in Sacramento, California, on 30 July, 1997. When she underwent a precautionary brain scan at the Davis Medical Center, a brain tumour was found. Doctors said the prognosis was good because they had found the tumour early.

ALVARO PASCUAL-LEONE and colleagues at the University of Valencia, Spain, have used a method called transcranial magnetic stimulation (TMS) on patients with severe drug-resistant depression. "Eleven of the 17 patients showed pronounced improvement that lasted for about two weeks after five days of daily TMS sessions," they wrote in the *Lancet*.

"No patient experienced any undesirable side-effects." The patients did not respond when the magnets were slightly displaced so that no magnetic effect was exerted on the brain. "TMS has advantages over electroconvulsive therapy," said the report. "It is practically painless, does not require anæsthesia, is not coupled with induction of a seizure, and has fewer risks and cognitive side-effects."

OPTHALMIC consultant Chris Canning, from Southampton, saved a woman's sight by removing a live 2cm worm from inside her eye during a 30-minute operation in Shantou, China. He brought the worm back to Britain for analysis.

A CHANCE REMARK by a patient led Dr Manohar Keswani, head of the burns department at Wadia Hospital for Children in Bombay, India, to discover that potato peelings enhanced the healing of serious burns without sticking to the wound. Over eight years, he developed the potato equivalent of a skin graft. "It allows wounds to heal much quicker than usual," he said. "It is a breakthrough and has saved lives," said the president of the British Burn Association. Potatoes seem to be very versatile veg. The Russian weekly *Argumenty i Facty* carried a novel hæmorrhoid cure: "Take a warm bath (35 degrees C), then lie down and insert a candle-shaped piece of raw potato into the anus for half an-hour." This solution is apparently infallible, but only if the patient has abstained from alcohol for at least 48 hours beforehand.

CRAB DUNG mixed with salt water or blood hardens to form a bone-like substance ideal for knitting together broken bones. It is more effective in mending limbs than metal or plastic inserts. Researchers at Reading University stumbled on the discovery while studying the effects of pollution on marine life.

SANDRA HOLLINGSWORTH, of Uttoxeter, suffered from chronic fatigue for over 30 years. In her 20s, it was diagnosed as a classic sign of diabetes, and she was even told she was mentally ill. Eventually, she visited alternative therapist Alan Halton, who suspected mercury poisoning from her 14 dental cavities. The electric current in her mouth was way above normal levels. After four operations to replace the fillings with a mercury-free white cement, Ms Hollingsworth began to recover. "I have become a different person," she said. "For the first time in my adult life, I feel great."

Twelve days after the Hollingsworth case was publicised, another case appeared. When her face swelled up over several months, Theresa Walker, 36, a telesales supervisor, was told she had a virus or possibly chickenpox. She became convinced her 59-year-old mother Cynthia was poisoning her, and turned on her. Theresa was sectioned and placed in a secure ward at the East Surrey Hospital in Redhill for four weeks. A tribunal then found nothing wrong with her, but when she went to a private clinic an accurate diagnosis was made. Ms Walker said: "The doctor took one look at my face and said 'You're being poisoned.'" Toxicology tests revealed 10 times the industrial limit of mercury in her body. After having her nine fillings out, she was put on medication to remove heavy metals from the brain and nervous system and advised not to drink tap water. "I feel so much better now," she said. "For years, I felt a kind of heaviness in my head, which must have been all the poison building up. I just feel so lucky that my mum stuck by me." Nicholas Warren, *FT*'s medical consultant, comments that the symptoms of neither woman conforms to the well-known features of heavy-metal poisoning, so why their condition improved is open to question.

MEDICAL DEVELOPMENTS

Parts of medical research are every bit as strange as the
weirdest reaches of forteana

A WOMAN known only as DR, who does not respond to fear,
anger, danger and suspense in real life or in films, provided a
clue about which part of the brain controls negative emotions.
The symptoms developed after surgery for epilepsy, in which
the left amygdala was destroyed and the right partially
destroyed. The amygdalæ are two almond-shaped structures
on either side of the brain in the temporal lobe, and the discovery contributes to the theory that emotions are controlled
from separate parts of the brain rather than one site, as was
previously thought.

TWO DENTISTS at the University of Maryland have discovered a jaw muscle overlooked by surgeons for 500 years. It
might explain mysterious links between sore jaws and pain

behind the eyes. Gwendolyn Dunn and Gary Hack were investigating temporomandibular joint (TMJ) disorder, the painful clicking in the lower jaw where it inserts into the skull. Anatomy books only showed the joint from the side, so they dissected a cadaver face first and found the unknown 1.5-inch-long muscle running between the jaw and a bony knob behind the eye socket. They have subsequently seen it in dozens of cadavers and magnetic resonance scans. Finding an undescribed muscle in the human head is like finding an overlooked elephant in the living room. Generations of surgeons have noticed this strip of tissue, but described it, incorrectly, as an extension of the temporalis, a muscle running from the side of the head. The two muscles are not only physically separated but distinct in every way, with separate nerves and blood supply. The new muscle, known so far only as 'he', is one of five involved in chewing, and the researchers believe it must help to lift and support the jaw.

SCIENTISTS have discovered that male human ears grow in seven-year cycles, reviving the ancient Greek belief that there are circaseptennial rhythms in human development. The discovery follows the revelation in 1995 that male ears continue to grow throughout life, at about 0.22mm a year in men over 30. Dr Jos Verhulst, from the Netherlands, and Patrick Onghena, from Belgium, writing in the *British Medical Journal*, said that they found that ear-growth velocity peaked around multiples of seven years. Earlier research by Verhulst, not yet published, shows that the fusion of the plates of the skull, causing the sutures between them to fade, follows the same seven-year pattern. It is believed that this circaseptennial rhythm also manifests in nose, chin and finger growth. Numerologists see seven as the sum of the spiritual three and the material four, signifying the Creation.

WHY are dreams always retrospective? Why do cosmonauts never dream about space? These and other questions are posed by two French researchers in *Le Grenier des Rêves*. According to psychologists, the 'day residue' in dreams is rather important. Half of all dreams refer to events in the preceding day and 89 per cent to events in the last 120 days. The older the event, the lower the odds that it will feature during the night. People who wear coloured glasses very quickly begin dreaming in the same colour. People who are, for instance, moving to a new place do not begin dreaming of the new location for weeks, even months. A Bassari from Senegal, who was resident in Paris for two extended stays, was asked to record his dreams. Surprisingly, 88 per cent of them were set in Africa and only six per cent featured France. This and other experiments are discussed at length, but explanations are lacking.

VIC TANDY, a CAL expert from Coventry University, was working late one night in a laboratory of a building he had been told was haunted. As he sat at the desk writing, he began to feel increasingly uncomfortable. He became aware that he was being watched, and an indistinct figure slowly emerged. He looked at it face-on, only to see it fade and vanish. He decided he must be cracking up, and went home. The following morning, Mr Tandy, a fencing enthusiast, noticed that a blade he had left clamped in a vice was vibrating wildly. Tests revealed a standing wave which reached a peak of intensity next to his desk, caused by a new extractor fan making the air vibrate at about 19Hz (cycles per second). Mr Tandy and Dr Tony Lawrence, of Coventry University's School of Health, published a report in the *Journal of the Society for Psychical Research* (**62**, 851, 360–364, April 1998). They discovered that infra-sound around this frequency had been linked to hyper-ventilation, triggering feelings of fear and anxiety (manifested in excessive perspiration and shivering), leading to further hyperventilation and so on – a classic panic attack. Research by NASA showed that the human eyeball has a resonant frequency of 18 cycles a second, at which it starts to vibrate in sympathy to infra-sound, causing a serious smearing of vision. "You probably need an object or a small movement in the periphery of your vision to start the phenomenon," said Mr Tandy, "then the brain may fill in details from your subconscious. If you are scared, the mind can play all kinds of tricks." Mr Tandy had since come across two more 'hauntings' where low-frequency sound might be to blame. The wind blowing over a window in a side wall of a long corridor might be enough to create a standing wave, similar to that formed by blowing over the neck of a bottle. The general reaction among psychic researchers was that infrasound was an useful variable to measure in hauntings, but that it was unlikely to account for more than a few specific cases.

EU-APPROVED CONDOMS have increased by a centimetre to 17cm, according to *Le Généraliste*, a Belgian medical journal. "It's not only height that has grown over decades," it added.

THEY may have grown, but if you use them too much, your brain shrinks. Dr Marc Breedlove (!), a psychologist from the University of California, found that male rats which spend a lot of time with sexually-receptive females suffer from a drop in the size of certain neurones. The effect, which he thinks is temporary, added to the growing evidence that variations between people's brains may be the result of sexual activity.

WOMEN may soon be able to grow their own breast implants rather than having them made from silicone. Doctors have developed a technique which uses tissue grown from the recipients' blood and fat cells to enlarge the breast. They have already succeeded in growing nipples this way.

THE MYSTERY of hill walkers and climbers – often young and healthy – found dead with no apparent cause may have been solved. Dr Michael Cherington and colleagues, from the Lightning Data Center in Denver, Colorado, studied the case of four golfers who were sheltering under a tree when it was struck by lightning. One suffered superficial burns, two were knocked unconscious but otherwise unhurt, and the fourth, a 32-year-old man, collapsed with a heart attack. A doctor who happened to be nearby gave him artificial resuscitation, but he died 18 days later without regaining consciousness. There was not a mark on him. Usually lightning deaths are the result of a direct strike, side flash or ground current, all of which leave signs of injury. In a letter to the *Lancet*, the Denver experts suggested that unexplained hill walker deaths are the result of near-miss lightning strikes generating a huge magnetic pulse. Lightning bolts generate currents of 100,000 amps or more, which can produce intense magnetic fields up to a metre around the point of impact. "The lightning may induce loop current within the human torso without evidence of current entering the body," according to the experts. "If these currents occur during a vulnerable part of the cardiac cycle, they could cause asystole [stopped heart beat] or ventricular fibrillation [an often fatal abnormal heart rhythm]." Weather forecasters advise that the most important thing to remember when caught in a thunderstorm is not to be the tallest object around. If you're in the open, lie down; and don't shelter under a tree.

MATTHEW MESSING, 16, was playing ice hockey in Quincy, Massachusetts, in 1995 when he was bumped. He collapsed and died instantly. The incident, along with nearly 70 others reported in recent years, had baffled doctors. In each case, they found no injury to the heart and no previous heart condition in the victims. Now the explanation for the rare deaths, which go by the medical name of *commotio cordis* – concussion of the heart – may have been found. In the *New England Journal of Medicine*, researchers suggest that the deaths result from an unusual conjunction of events. When the heart is beating, there is a fleeting moment, about a hundredth of a second long, when the electrical rhythm is resetting, so to speak, just before a beat. During that moment, if a moderate blow is directed to exactly the spot on the chest above the heart, the electrical rhythm breaks and the heart stops beating, fibrillating ineffectively. If the blow is too strong or too weak, or the timing is a few milliseconds off, death is averted.

WILLIAM BURROUGHS' horrific Dr Benway may have been right after all – a toilet plunger can be a help when you have a heart attack. According to a study in St Paul, Minnesota, working with a toilet plunger on someone who has suffered a cardiac arrest saved significantly more victims (59%) than standard cardiopulmonary resuscitation techniques (33%).

A WOMAN who was attacked by a swan while feeding birds in a park helped contribute to a new advance in medicine. The 32-year-old woman went to hospital when her finger became swollen and took on a strange deep blue colour after being "pecked viciously." On examination, doctors found the wound was infected with a rare kind of bacterium which produces a deep blue pigment and which would not respond to regular antibiotics. They had to use a drug called ciprofloxacin to kill off the bug, and as a consequence it has been recommended for use in all cases of bites by aquatic animals.

EXTRA! EXTRA! READ ALL ABOUT IT

All sorts of people get born with extra bits, but few would ever know

SEGUNDINA JIMENA claims her three children, like her late husband, have 'gills' and can stay under water for six minutes, according to the Philippine newspaper *The Sun-Star Daily*. The 'gills' consist of small holes on the sides of the neck below each ear. Dr Antonio Yapha, chairman of the Cebu provincial health committee, planned to visit the family in Dumanjug, about 350 miles south of Manilla, to investigate. "If it is a congenital anomaly, I will convince them to see a pulmonary specialist," he said. Mrs Jimena said she didn't know how to swim, and her children were just starting to learn. The family lives in a remote mountain village far from the sea. According to a TV report from Cebu, one of the children, Hipolito, said liquid passes through the holes whenever they drink. The holes enlarge when they go underwater, allowing them to stay submerged for six minutes. Bizarre medical stories are very popular in the Philippines.

SAMANTHA EVANS was born in September 1996 at East Glamorgan Hospital in Pontyprydd. She was the fifth child for David, 36, and Allyson, 31, from Beddau, Mid-Glamorgan, and it wasn't until her first feed that they noticed she had 12 fingers and toes – identical middle digits on each hand and foot. "It doesn't bother her, and most people don't notice," said Mrs Evans. "The main problem will be finding shoes that fit." Babies born with an extra finger or toe (a condition known as polydactyly) are relatively common. It is much rarer to have two fully-formed extra digits on both hands and both feet, as in this case. There is no history of polydactyly in the families of either of Samantha's parents. A plastic surgeon was to examine the child to decide whether her extra digits should be removed, but they were so perfectly formed that they may well not do so. Before Samantha, Denise Stretton, of Dunstable in Bedfordshire, was allegedly the last person born in Britain with 12 fingers and toes. In her case, it was less surprising, as her father, sister, aunt, uncle and grandfather all had extra fingers. Denise's extra fingers were removed when she was two days old. At 13, her extra toes went as well. "I never had any problems walking, but I was given the choice and decided I'd rather have them off," she said.

ABOUT 75 members of the 300-strong Koli-Patel clan in the small western Indian village of Golida have six or more fingers on each hand. Shisabhai Koli Patel, the clan's 70-year-old patriarch, has variously claimed that his kinsfolk are victims of a curse put on them by a local goddess called Mataji, or by a six-fingered witch doctor. The Koli-Patels are probably an inbred sect, reinforcing a recessive gene for polydactyly. They believe they are descendants of South American Indians who were brought to India centuries ago as slaves.

A BABY born in Britain in 1983 had a 2in tail which moved, according to a report in the *British Medical Journal*. This was thought to be a unique occurrence, as other cases of people born with tails usually involve no more than an immobile fatty lump at the base of the spine. The delivery team were amazed, and with the agreement of the parents, the appendage was surgically removed. In all other ways the baby was normal. The scar healed completely, and it is unlikely that the child will ever be told.

A HOSPITAL in Fujian, China, found that a man of 23 (or 25), named only as Deng, had three eyes, the first such case ever recorded in China. The third eye, on his left temple, had an eyebrow, eyelid, eyelashes, a tear gland and a pupil which moved in synch with his other eyes, according to Dr Zheng Yizhong. However, Deng was blind in his left eye and his third eye. This was said to be the third known case of a three-eyed person, according to Shanghai's *Xinmin Wanbao* newspaper.

ALSO IN CHINA, surgeons operated on a man with three tongues, removing two of them so he can eat and speak normally for the first time in 20 years, according to the Xichuan newsagency. Xian Shihua, a peasant farmer from the south-western province of Xichuan, was born with one tongue, but a second, smaller one grew when he was five years old, and later, a third. His largest was 13in long, 6in wide, and 4.4in thick, while the other two were 3.6in long and of varying widths and thicknesses. The bizarre operation, carried out at the Southwest Military Hospital in Chongqing city, enabled Xian to speak normally to family and friends and to go off the liquid diet on which he had subsisted since childhood. Xian's doctors said he had been suffering from a benign tumour, but his condition was the first they had encountered.

JOSE MARIA LOPEZ born in Mexico and living in Whittier, California, spent most of his 33 years hiding a third foot that protruded from his ankle, wearing baggy trousers to cover the 6in (15cm) appendage. After a surgeon amputated it for free, Lopez said he was feeling fantastic and looked forward to buying his first boots.

ZHANG XINGZHI, a boy from Guangdong province in China, was born with three feet. The extra one was removed in a five-hour operation with the help of Hong Kong specialists. We are reminded of a recent quotation from the *Fulham & Hammersmith Chronicle*: "There was an air of expectancy as I pruned myself in front of the mirror."

AN EGYPTIAN TEENAGER who complained of stomach pains had his parasitic twin fœtus (*fœtus-in-fœtu*) lodged in a sac pressing against his kidneys. Doctors in Cairo found the seven-inch fœtus, weighing 4.4lb, with a head, arm, tongue and fully-formed teeth, when they operated on building worker Hisham Ragab, 16. The size of the internal twin suggested that it had survived to 32 or 33 weeks' gestation. Incomplete ovum division is not uncommon, but this was the most developed fœtus ever found in Egypt. Hisham was reported to be well and recovering from his operation.

DOCTORS in Esztergom, Hungary, who treated a teenager stabbed in a fight, thought he would die because the knife had apparently penetrated his heart. However, the 18-year-old, identified only as VJ, had his heart on the right-hand side. "He was born under a lucky star," said a doctor as the youth recovered in hospital.

Doctors in Columbia examining healthy Dario Rios, 30, made a similar discovery after he complained of a pain in his side. They found that most of his major organs are on the wrong side of his body.

DOCTORS in the northern Indian city of Meerut, found a uterus and ovaries while operating on Mihammed Zafrul, 35, to remove a tumour in his stomach. The *Hindustan Times* quoted gynæcologist Dr Vinita Agarwal as saying that the uterus was fully developed and could sustain pregnancy. Mr Zafrul, although married for 10 years, had no children because of a testicular tumour. The uterus and ovaries were removed for biopsy.

PERUVIAN RADIO ANNOUNCER José Vasquez, 25, born with two penises, has refused to let doctors remove one because "both are a gift of God". He claimed that his audience has soared since he told listeners about his unusual endowment.

A BABY GIRL with two heads was born in My Tho, the capital of the southern Vietnamese province of Tien Giang. The baby, which weighed 8lb 6oz, had two heads, two hearts, two spines, but only one set of reproductive organs and lungs, one liver, two arms and two legs. In keeping with the father's wishes, the 27-year-old mother was not told of the baby's defects. Two days after the birth, the baby was moved to the main Ho Chi Minh City children's hospital. She was on oxygen because of a heart complication, but was otherwise healthy and was doing well. Sadly, she died a month later.

CHAPTER FIVE

IN GERMANY, a 30-year-old Iranian woman gave birth to a baby boy with two heads. Doctors discovered the abnormality when the woman had trouble giving birth. Experts said the child, believed at the time to be the only living two-headed person in the world, would survive. The brains in the two heads functioned independently, so one could be asleep while the other was screaming, but it was possible to nourish the infant by feeding him through one mouth at a time. The mother, who had three other normal children, was not allowed to see the baby. In Nalla Sopara, near Mumbai (Bombay) in western India, another two-headed child was born in early 1999. The child had only one heart, and its parents declined to identify its gender. The family refused requests to surgically remove one head, saying the baby was a reincarnation of the Hindu god Vishnu.

A CHINESE BABY BOY with two brains was reported to be doing well, but hardly slept because his brains worked in rotation, according to the Xinhua news agency. The boy, who was born in Chaoyang city in north-eastern Liaoning province, China, in July 1995, was growing well and did not need surgery, doctors said. He slept for about an hour a night but sometimes for as little as 20 minutes.

WHEN ALYSHIA COLLIER was born at Southmead Hospital in Bristol on 30 September, 1997, she had two teeth. "The midwives said they had never seen a baby born with teeth before – it is supposed to be very lucky," said 21-year-old mother Sally, of Bedminster Down, Bristol. "The doctors said the teeth would drop out and that she would get milk teeth at the right age, but they just get bigger and bigger. She even had a teething rattle for Christmas." Ashley Sinclair was born in Boston, Lincolnshire, in 1989 with two front teeth; and in June

1990, Sean Kenny was born in Basingstoke with 12 teeth, believed to be a world record. Three days later, doctors pulled them to prevent possible feeding problems. Sean grew a full second set of teeth at 18 months. In October 1991, Beverly Carter's baby was born with two teeth at St. James's Hospital in Leeds. Phillip Mejia was born with a single tooth in Racine, Wisconsin, on 7 March 1995, but it was loose and was pulled two days later. In March 1996, Emma Louise Shepherd was born in Scotland with two teeth; these were also loose and were soon after removed. Incisors normally appear at 5–8 months, molars at 24 months. In 1956, Robert Clinton was reported to have a molar tooth at one month by staff at Bellvue Hospital New York.

These reports strengthen the view that such cases are in fact supernumerary dentitions rather than just the early eruption of milk teeth. Some celebrated men are supposed to have been born with teeth. Louis XIV (1638–1715) was accredited with having two teeth at birth. Bigot, a physician and philosopher of the 16th century; Henry Boyd, the poet (d.1832); the 3rd century Roman Emperor Valerian; and Richard III (1452–85) were all reported to have had this anomaly.

OF COURSE, not everyone is born with extra bits; some just grow them along the way, which is what happened to an American returning from a trip to the Virgin Islands. He grew breasts. Dr Tricia McNair suggested that he had eaten too much chicken fed on oestrogen, then drunk too much alcohol, which prevents the liver breaking down the hormone. "Alcoholics often grow breasts," she explained helpfully.

CHAPTER SIX

INEXPLICABLE!

Medical science often claims to have an explanation for everything, but some phenomena are just beyond explanation...

FRANK KULCZYNSKI, 76, collapsed in his garden in McKeesport near Pittsburgh on 25 April 1994. His son said he had been fertilising his lawn. Two hospital workers developed rashes when they touched him. Others complained of headaches or other ailments. Four were hospitalised overnight for observation and released with no symptoms. The man's skin was hot, although he had no fever; it was also blistering and peeling, and blood poured from his mouth. One hospital worker reported an ammonia-like odour; another said the patient smelled of chlorine. A possible insect bite was noted on his neck when he was brought in. Kulczynski died in hospital, and a high-security autopsy was planned.

IN LURNEA, near Sydney in Australia, a 44-year-old man, who died after swallowing 100 rat poison tablets, forced the evacuation of the emergency unit at Liverpool Hospital, west of Sydney, when his body started emitting a deadly gas. Experts said three tablets of the fumigant would have killed him. He was found unconscious down a roadside embankment in the suburb of Leppington on 5 November, 1998, and died soon after in hospital. Within an hour, the body began emitting a pungent odour, and about 20 people in the unit became nauseous. The man had taken aluminium phosphide tablets, which dissolved in his body to emit phosphine, a lethal fumigant used to rid grain silos of rodents and weevils, which can be fatal to humans at only three parts per million of air. The fire brigade and hazardous chemicals unit closed the hospital ward and switched off the air conditioning. Firefighters wearing protective clothing and breathing apparatus sealed the body in a hazardous chemical suit and packed it in a toxic waste drum before it was taken to a nearby mortuary.

A 30-YEAR-OLD MAN from Cardiff, who worked in a factory dressing chickens, pricked his finger to the bone in September 1991. The tiny scratch became inflamed and his GP identified cellulitis (a simple bacterial infection) and prescribed antibiotics. The inflammation did not clear up, and the finger began to smell putrid. The inflammation eventually went down, but the smell became worse and spread to the whole body. A skin biopsy revealed *clostridia*, a spore-forming variety of bacteria found in soil and the intestinal tracts of humans and animals. It is also responsible for causing gangrene in deep wounds and can result in death, but had not been found in the skin before. Clostridia are normally sensitive to antibiotics, but every kind was tried without success: the pong could not be budged. Dressing the man in a charcoal-lined jacket like a giant odour-eater also failed. The case was written up in the *Lancet* in November, 1996, in the hope that an expert somewhere would be able to solve the mystery. Meanwhile, the man was a virtual prisoner in his parents' home; the overpowering stench made people recoil. "It is a smell so putrid it is like going into a pantry and finding food that should have been thrown out a long time ago," said Dr Peter Holt, consultant dermatologist at the University Hospital of Wales in Cardiff.

IN INDIA in 1994, dozens of people died of what seemed to be the Plague, but, according to the *Lancet*, after investigations by medical researchers they decided it was probably not the Plague after all, but was caused by completely different bacteria which mimic its symptoms. Eh?

A MYSTERY ailment which caused students to hallucinate, shout, wail and hurt themselves affected 27 pupils out of 1,000 at the Tamale Business Secondary School in the northern Ghana town of Tamale. It was temporarily closed. According to the *Ghanaian Times*, 11 pupils at two other secondary schools in the town had been treated for similar symptoms in the previous four days. The victims said they had visions of an old lady beckoning them.

IN TANZANIA, two schools had to be closed after children were seized by an affliction which caused them to collapse in fits of uncontrollable laughter. The regional medical officer in the Mara region of Northern Tanzania, on Lake Victoria, found 40 victims of the disease among schoolchildren. It became impossible for classes to continue.

DOCTORS were baffled and resorted to blaming witchcraft, sorcery or aliens when faced with the strange case of Opani Banda, 14, in Malawi. Several days after an accident which required her to have stitches, she returned to the hospital in the central Nkhotakhota district of Malawi to have them removed, then went home. The next morning, however, the stitches had reappeared, so she returned to the hospital to have them removed again, but by mid-afternoon they were back. The sutures did not just appear on the wound, but randomly down the left side of her body from head to toe. The family consulted a witch doctor, who also failed to get rid of them.

THE FACT that humans (unlike some monkeys) can't tickle themselves intrigued Charles Darwin, who could think of no plausible evolutionary explanation. It remains a true biological mystery, although a tickling machine designed 20 years ago by Dr L Weiskrantz of the Department of Experimental Psychology at Oxford demonstrated that the 'feedback information' from the movement of the arm was more important in cancelling out the sensation of being tickled than the person's knowledge that he was trying to tickle himself.

A 99-YEAR-OLD woman in Shengxian, Zhejiang province, eastern China, sprouted horns. They started growing on Zhang Taofeng's head after she developed a lump on her forehead in 1992. One horn disappeared in 1995, but a replacement then grew.

A FURNITURE RESTORER from Lucca in Tuscany, known by the pseudonym 'Elena Cappelli', fell into a coma for three weeks in 1983 at the age of 31, after suffering a fit of asphyxia from chemical fumes while polishing furniture. According to the Roman magazine *Liberal*, which dubbed her the 'Sleeping Beauty', she had stopped ageing after coming round from the coma over 15 years ago. "After I came out of hospital, I had a strange feeling of strength," she said. "I felt very clearly that something had changed in my metabolism. Until today, I have not talked to anyone about this for fear of seeming crazy." Medical specialists have pondered whether her condition might really have been triggered by something other than the coma. It could, for example, have been a case of juvenalism, a form of biological behaviour similar to that of certain animals such as the marmot – which lives twice as long as rabbits thanks to a form of hibernation. Apparently 'Cappelli' had looked so young when she sat her exam as a restorer at the age of 28, even before the coma, that the invigilators asked for her ID, thinking she was under-age. "Perhaps what we have here is a case of retarded rather than accelerated ageing."

Local journalists could not locate the Sleeping Beauty and some suspected a *mezza-bufala* (practical joke). *Liberal,* however, insisted the story was true.

THERE ARE REPORTS that allergic reactions can be induced by suggestion. An artificial rose, for instance, can induce an allergy to roses. According to a report in *Science*: "The possibility that histamine may be released as a learned response has now been tested. In a classical conditioning procedure in which an immunologic challenge was paired with the presentation of an odour, guinea pigs showed a plasma histamine increase when presented with the odour alone. This suggests that the immune response can be enhanced through the activity of the central nervous system."

A 70-YEAR-OLD woman who was taking 12 aspirins a day for her arthritis and otosclerosis (an ear disease which causes deafness) kept hearing songs from the 1930s and 1940s. She had requested 'When Irish Eyes are Smiling' for her funeral, but cancelled her request after hearing it in her head 50 times. The sounds continued even after she was put in a soundproof room. Cutting her aspirin dose in half ended the unwelcome concert. Aspirin sometimes causes ringing in the ears, but this was the first case on record of someone hearing whole tunes hour after hour, wrote Dr James Allen in the *New England Journal of Medicine*.

IF IT HAD been Mozart she was hearing rather than popular songs, it might have done her some good. According to a report from the University of California published in *Nature*, listening to Mozart can raise your intelligence. They found that 10 minutes of Mozart's sonata for two pianos in D major improved the IQ scores of 36 volunteers by an average of nine points. Prior exposure to silence or simple sounds, such as a relaxation tape, had little effect. "We predict that music lacking complexity or which is repetitive may interfere with rather than enhance abstract reasoning," the researchers said. The catch is, however, that the effect wears off after 15 minutes. Even more extraordinary is the claim made by a Japanese pharmaceuticals company. They market Mozart as a cure for baldness. The Daiichi company's hair tonic, shampoo and conditioner sells for $56 and comes with a compact disc of Mozart. A spokesman claimed that tests demonstrated that Mozart's French Horn Concerto No 3, Concerto for Flute and Harp, and Piano Concerto No 21 are "Music friendly to your hair," and, combined with hair tonic, are effective in restoring hair. The guinea pigs, follicularly-challenged men aged 36–44, were put in a capsule and had Mozart's music played to them while brainwaves, temperature and pulse readings were monitored. The company spokesman did admit that no noticeable hair growth was reported, and one sceptical doctor pointed out that music simply relieved stress: "When you are relaxed, you are in a better condition to grow hair back."

ODD INJURIES, STRANGE SYMPTOMS

Nature is capable of infinite strangeness, as this collection
of surreal sufferings attests

A HONG KONG woman and her two daughters were in critical condition in hospital after giving mouth-to-mouth resuscitation to their dog when it passed out after being washed with a shampoo containing amitrax, which is normally used to rid cattle and sheep of ticks. The dog died.

SEVENTEEN people were injured by a lightning bolt as they sheltered under a tree during a football match in Aylesford, Kent, on 2 September 1995. It was thought to be Britain's biggest multiple lighnting strike. Many were thrown into the air, and 14 were treated for injuries including cardiac arrest, paralysis of the legs, ruptured eardrums, spinal damage, double vision, confusion, amnesia, psychological trauma and psychosis. All eventually recovered. Ten of the victims had a distinctive pattern (never before recorded) of miniature haem-orrhages or small burn holes, about the size of a match head, on each toe and at one-inch intervals around the soles of the feet. "They were quite deep and fairly painful," said one victim. The phenomenon was dubbed 'tip-toe signs'.

AN UNIDENTIFIED MAN in his late 20s walked into a police station in Ohio with a 9in wire protruding from his forehead and asked officers to give him an X-ray to help him find his brain. The man had drilled a six-inch hole in his skull with a power drill, and had stuck the wire in to try and find the brain.

JOSEPH MORAN, 53, sued the makers of Viagra for $110 million after he claimed the impotence drug caused blue flashes from his fingertips as he was driving, which made him crash his car.

DR ELLIF DAHL'S study of 1,051 animal bites in Oslo, Norway, between 1993 and 1995 has shown that 60 per cent of dog bite victims were men, 70 per cent of cat bite victims were women and 68 per cent of horse bite victims were girls.

A MAN held at the state mental hospital in Little Rock, Arkansas, used either his fingers or sunglasses to pull out one of his eyes and flush it down a lavatory after being ruled competent to stand trial. After being treated, he gouged out the other eye on 18 November. After he pulled out the first eye, his hands were chained to a belt at his waist, but he managed to lower his head enough to pull out the other eye.

AN ELDERLY HUNGARIAN man returned his new dentures because they broadcast a radio programme day and night; the metal parts acted as a radio receiver. The problem was solved by lacing the man's mouth with extra-thin wire to short-circuit the gadget.

MAHENDRA VALLAND, a 45-year-old engineer from Leicester, began hiccuping after a vindaloo curry on 19 February 1998. A glass of water seemed to cure the problem; but that evening, after a second curry, he began to hiccup in earnest and none of the usual remedies worked. After a week, desperate and exhausted, he was admitted to hospital, but it took another week, until 5 March, before the hiccups were stopped with a course of antacid tablets. "I was hiccuping every four seconds," he said. "The curry was quite hot, but nothing out of the ordinary for me, so it's a mystery why they started." The *St Louis (MO) Medical and Surgical Journal* (xlvii, 377) recorded a man of 35 who 'hiccoughed' for 12 years; and in 1996, there was a report of a Dane who had been afflicted for nine years. The world champion, however, is Charlie Osborne (1894–1991) of Anthon, Ohio, who started hiccuping in 1922. He stopped on 5 June 1990 – 68 years later – after three days of "fierce praying" by his daughter, and died 11 months later. Several people, including one pope, have died from hiccups.

A STUNNING ASSORTMENT of items have been found inserted in the human body where the sun don't shine, includ-ing a rolled-up magazine, various vegetables, a jeweller's saw, assorted frozen animal parts and... a human hand and fore-arm. One supposes that this limb was the result of some eso-teric yoga practice, rather than belonging to another person who may or may not have been attached to its other end, although we wouldn't be too sure. We are not told, but many of these instances come with explanations that are even more bizarre than the objects themselves. The fortean files bulge with accounts of anomalous objects found inside the human body. In a recent paper on the 'Management of colorectal foreign bodies', Drs J Cohen and J Sackier examined 49 cases from an 11-year period. While a small number were due to accidents, smuggling, well-intentioned remedies for constipation and violent assault, 38 resulted from sexual acts and most of these were down to auto-eroticism. Instances were "often referred to humorously," noted the authors, yet there were occasional fatalities. In this, they likened the phenomenon to the use of electrocution as an aid to climax.

A MIDDLE-AGED JAPANESE MAN went to his doctor complaining of a painful sensation in his mouth and throat. He had numerous small spindle-shaped structures embedded in the mucosal tissue, which were thought to be some kind of parasite until detailed examination revealed that they were spermatophores from a squid, which the man had previously eaten raw as sushi. Several species of squid are known to produce projectile spermatophores. Under normal circumstances, the male shoots them into the skin of the female. It is not known what species of squid the man ate – but it wasn't a giant squid, whose 8in-long spermatophores might have done more than provoke a sore throat.

THINGS INSIDE

A stunning variety of things get inside the human body,
whether by accident or design, and manage to do
extraordinary things while in there too

YETER YILDERIM, a Turkish teenager, was withdrawn and
moody, and suffered from violent headaches and mysterious
stomach pains. When the local folk healers failed to cure her,
her parents took her to hospital in Ankara, 80 miles away,
where the doctors X-rayed her and discovered three water
snakes "slightly thicker than string and nearly a foot long" living in her stomach. In a credibility-stretching case, a Syrian
woman, Khadija el Reefi, suffered from excruciating pains
which were caused by a six-foot snake wedged in her
intestines. It, apparently, cheeped like a chicken when it was
hungry. Surgery in Syria and then in Spain failed to remove
the snake, after which the story petered out. Both stories are
strongly reminiscent of ancient tales of bosom serpents which
lodged themselves in people's innards.

SIX-YEAR-OLD Sarah Jayne Tait, from Edinburgh, came home from school with her left eye swollen and painful. Neither her teachers nor her family could see what was wrong, and doctors at the Sick Children's Hospital drew a blank too. Then a specialist at the Eye Pavilion inserted a probe behind her eye and out popped a baked bean. Sarah Jayne, who wasn't keen on beans, had no idea how it got there.

MAJOR RICHARD BINGLEY, of Newton Abbot in Devon, was admitted to a London eye hospital in December 1988 to have the pain behind his left eye investigated. He had been shot in the thigh four times in 1952 during the Korean War, but medics had found only three exit wounds. The remaining bullet took 36 years to meander to behind his eye. Surgeons removed the bullet, and the hospital kept it for their museum. Ilija Sesum's bullet hung around even longer. He was wounded in a World War I battle near the Italian–Austrian border in 1916. During an illnesss in 1981, when he was 90, the Yugoslav coughed for over two hours and dislodged the bullet which had been inside him for 65 years. He felt fine afterwards.

ALSO FINDING a stray bullet was a 17-year-old French girl, named only as Isabelle, who was rushed to hospital when she started hallucinating. A scan showed a .22-calibre rifle bullet in her brain. Her mother remembered that when the girl was 15 months old, she had come into the house with blood spurting from her head; a doctor had simply applied a bandage. A similar case occurred in Sweden, where doctors who had been unsuccessfully treating a 10-year-old girl for an infected insect bite for six weeks removed a .22 rifle bullet from her thigh. The girl's family said they did not know how she was shot. The girl had felt a pain in her leg while playing outside her home and had looked down to see an insect crawling from her jeans.

RATHER MORE RISKY was the situation in which Hoang Minh Son, 36, found himself. Working in his fields, he accidentally set off a US-made shell left over from the Vietnam war. It detonated and launched an egg-sized grenade which lodged, but didn't explode, in his left arm. He was taken – very carefully – to hospital, where the live M-79 grenade was removed by army surgeons in "an extremely tense" operation.

IN A LETTER to the *Bradford Argus*, Mrs Jack Crackers described how her husband, then 75, had choked on a sweet while they were in Sweden. She had given him a good thump on the back and a bus ticket, issued in Buxton (Derbyshire) on 2 May, 1927, shot out of his ear. Her husband, who had "been troubled by deafness" for most of his life, thought he must have stuck it in his ear on his way home from school. Similarly, Alfred Rison, 16, was cured of deafness in his right ear when doctors in Wisconsin found he'd had a pebble stuck in it since he was four. In Wrexham, a former miner's deafness was cured when his doctor took a lump of coal from his ear. The coal dropped into a kidney dish when GP Arik Shaik syringed the man's ear. The 83-year-old man had been deaf for 20 years, but had been unaware of the cause.

JULIA SCHUMANSKY, from Hartsville, Tennessee, noticed "a little knot on my backside" in July 1989, but did not worry about it until it started jutting out of her left buttock. Urgent surgery was carried out to see whether the lump was a malignant tumour, but it turned out to be a four-inch pork chop bone. Judging by the amount of tissue which had grown around it, the bone had been there for five to 10 years; her physician speculated that Julia's bulk – she was 5ft 1in tall and weighed 217lbs – had prevented her from feeling the initial penetration.

WHEN DOCTORS operated on Joseph Miral, 62, for suspected lung cancer, they found something they hadn't bargained for instead – his false teeth. Miral, from Lyon, France, explained that he'd lost them in a car crash 15 years before and they'd never been found.

DOCTORS in Stockton, California, found a one-inch sprig of Christmas tree in Tracy McIntyre's right lung. It had been there for almost 15 years, but was as green as ever. Since Christmas 1980, when 18-month-old Tracy suffered a choking fit near the tree, she'd had breathing difficulties, coughing fits and bad breath. Finally her parents took her to hospital.

MARIE HEFFERMAN also suffered long-term side effects from Christmas. She was 13 when she and her family celebrated their first Christmas in Australia in 1972. Six weeks later, she developed laryngitis and lost her voice. X-rays failed to show the silver threepenny bit she had swallowed while eating her Christmas pudding – it lay horizontally between her vocal chords, preventing their vibration. Twelve years later, a coughing fit brought up a small black lump which turned out to contain the unsuspected coin. After speech therapy, she found she could speak... with an Australian accent.

SURGEONS operating on 67-year-old Janet Webb's 'tumour' in Cedar Rapids, Iowa, found a diamond ring, lost 44 years earlier during a Cæsarean operation. The same thing happened to Virginia Argue in Roseville, California, six months earlier. She had carried a diamond ring in her stomach for 50 years.

YVETTE MOREL was unaware for 48 years that a sliver of glass was lodged in her stomach. It happened when she rode her bike into a plate glass window at the age of eight. Doctors removed the shard after discovering it during a routine X-ray at Lure, eastern France.

HAIRDRESSER Theo Georgiou's gut problem was caused by something much smaller. After he collapsed with agonising stomach pain, doctors operated on him and found the source of his trouble was a half-inch hair. They believed it had worked its way in through his navel. Theo, 26, from Birmingham, had been suffering steadily worsening pain for months. "They'd never seen anything like it and told me it was a million-to-one chance," he said. "I'd never thought of hairdressing as dangerous before, but now I'll be more careful."

MARTIN HALL would sympathise, though. Martin, 35, a barber from Bristol, had to have an operation to remove customers' hair from between his fingers. He said, "One hair got stuck in my right hand, leaving an opening. Other hairs got into the wound and it gradually got worse. Eventually it went septic and I had an operation. It will be another month before I can return to work."

ALSO having hair trouble was an unnamed 22-year-old woman from Phoenix, Arizona, who had to be operated on to remove a football-size ball of hair from her stomach. It had gradually built up, due to her habit of nervously chewing her hair. Even stranger, though, was the five-inch hairball removed from a French woman's stomach – she told them it was a result of her habit of licking her pet poodle to make him nice and clean.

X-RAYS failed to show why a 95-year-old woman was having trouble swallowing. Her symptoms worsened, so she underwent emergency throat surgery. To his amazement, the doctor found that the cause of the problem was a rosary, complete with crucifix, lodged in her throat. They hadn't realised this was the problem when they X-rayed, as they had assumed the rosary was being worn around the woman's throat.

RODERICK ALLSOP had been troubled with watering eyes for five years, when a routine X-ray revealed the reason. The seven-year-old had an open safety-pin stuck up his nose.

ON THE OTHER end of the scale is the case of a young man who was operated on for a tender lump on the side of his neck. Surgeons removed a small piece of plastic looking rather like a fang. According to the report in the *British Journal of Surgery*, the man recalled being bitten by a woman dressed as a vampire at a Hallowe'en party the previous year.

PAUL HURD JR, a respected expert on North American bees, spent two summers in Alaska in the early 1950s collecting a number of tundra insects, mainly gnats, midges, springtails, rove beetles, flies and wasps. To catch these creatures, Hurd used an aspirator. By carefully inhaling, an entomologist can suck up an assortment of specimens, transferring them to a glass jar for later study. A fine-mesh screen usually covers the end of the tube through which the operator inhales. This keeps any aspirated insects from being sucked out of the vial and accidentally swallowed. In Hurd's case, a fine-mesh screen wasn't enough. About two months after completing the summer's work, Hurd became ill. Over the course of the following week, a whole selection of insects came out – alive – from his left sinus. These included three adult rove beetles, 13 fungus gnat larvæ, three egg parasitic wasps and about 50 springtails, Hurd explained in the 4 June 1954, issue of the journal *Science*. "It is believed that these protracted periods of daily aspiration during the summer contributed to a case of *myiasis* [fly maggots infesting a body cavity] that is without parallel in its origin and nature," Hurd noted. According to Hurd, none of the insects that emerged from his head was previously known to cause myiasis in humans. Apparently these tiny insects gained access as even tinier eggs, which easily passed through the aspirator's fine-mesh screen. "Admittedly," he wrote, "it is almost unbelievable that the insects should have undergone several stages in their metamorphosis within the sinuses, but since the screen was so fine as to preclude the possibility of the aspiration of adult insects, it must be concluded that such was the case."

SIMILAR HORRORS were suffered by Australian scientist Andrew Sheppard when a bot-fly sprayed its larvæ into his eye while he examined it. Sheppard had to endure hours of pain as the larvæ used their hooks to crawl round his right eyeball. Doctors could see nothing there and sent him home with eyewash, but he realised the larvæ were afraid of the light and had hidden behind his eyeball. He turned off the light, enticing them to crawl round the front again, where his wife was able to blot all 15 of the critters off.

EVEN WORSE was the case of a man who arrived at the doctors complaining of discomfort in his right ear. When doctors looked in his ear, the canal was full of maggots feeding on wax, inflamed skin and his eardrum. Doctors filled the ear with castor oil, and one by one the maggots floated out. They were identified as belonging to green-bottle flies, making it probable he'd acquired them a few days before when he'd fallen asleep, drunk, on a seaweed-strewn beach.

ODD MEDICINES

There is no end to the things people will take in the belief
that they will cure themselves of something

TWO MOZAMBICANS, Amerko Manyike, 23, and Phelex
Chauke, 24, were arrested in South Africa's Northern Province
and found to be carrying a bag containing human testicles.
They were charged with murdering Thomas Mthuki, 21, the
owner of the testicles, whose body was found in a shallow
grave near the men's squatter camp. The killers had tried to
sell the testicles for £1,000 to a witch doctor for use as *muti*, a
traditional medicine.

ACCORDING TO the Hong Kong newspaper *Ta Kung Pao*,
people in China are consuming "the dried flesh of celestial
beings", convinced that it can prevent cancer. The elixir comes
from the city of Wushan, where a man discovered it 40 years
ago. His daughter, who suffered from a bone disease, is said to
have been cured by the substance, which her father thought-
fully pickled in a barrel of rice wine.

ALSO IN HONG KONG, human fœtuses have become a fashionable cure-all, with at least one state-run clinic giving them away to women who consider them a tonic. The fœtuses, usually a few months old, are the result of abortions. "They can make your skin smoother, your body stronger, and are good for your kidneys," said a doctor at the city's Sin Hua clinic, who then helpfully added that she personally liked her fœtuses with pork soup.

RESEARCHERS into Chinese traditional medicine have decided that mole rat bones are just as effective as tiger bones in treating arthritis and rheumatism. This means that poachers and illegal hunters who have reduced the world population of wild tigers to about 5,000 can start trading in rats instead – and there are more than 200 million mole rats in China alone. However, 16 former employees at an abattoir in Wagga Wagga, Australia, were charged with stealing gallstones from dead cows, which were believed to be destined for the Chinese medicine market. They are worth almost as much as gold on the Chinese medicine market, up to £9 a gram. They are used for "controlling fever and cleansing the blood circulation system," according to Alice Import Export, one of the companies buying up the stones.

IN TAIPEI, Taiwan, relatives of hardened drinkers are flocking to a new cure for alcoholism – tiger excrement. The dung is dried and ground into a powder, mixed with wine, and served to the unsuspecting drinker. Zoo director Wen Yung-chang said that most of the people going for the cure were "women asking for tiger fæces to help their husbands or relatives stop drinking... Those who are too fond of drinking should watch out. Maybe their next cup will contain tiger droppings!" We're not sure whether this is more of a deterrent than a cure.

A SCIENTIFIC STUDY in the USA reported in *New Scientist* claims cocaine could boost the immune system and kill off *E coli*. It was found that adding wacky dust to mouse cells helped them to fight bacteria, including *E coli*. Elsewhere, Professor John Rosencrans, who issued a report claiming that nicotine could help fight diseases such as Alzheimer's and Parkinson's, and alleviate depression and anxiety, has been condemned by the anti-smoking lobby.

IN 1964, Yan Zhongshan started collecting ants, washing them in pure water, drying and cooking them, and making them into pills. He lost his teeth when he was 72; by the age of 87, he had new ones – sharp enough to crack nuts with – and exceptionally sharp hearing.

IN CHINA'S Jinlin province, peasant Wang Biao cured himself of convulsions by eating more than 1,800 live poisonous snakes over a two-year period. Although he is now cured of the convulsions, Wang is addicted to the snakes and has to have one before every meal. He has started breeding them to ensure he has enough to last him through the winter.

CURATIVE POWERS are being claimed for a spring on Prince Edward Island, British Columbia. Art Doyle, now in his mid 70s, says that the spring cleared up the pain from a chronic knee injury in 1994. Buddy MacAdam, 73, began drinking the water some years ago after he was diagnosed as seriously ill; he needed a coronary bypass, but doctors felt that his veins were not in sufficiently good shape for surgery. After 40 days of drinking water from the spring, he reports, he was examined again and the surgeons changed their mind and operated successfully. The spring has been associated with 'miracle' cures for at least a century and a half; it is widely believed in the area that it was once blessed by Bishop Angus MacEachern, a Roman Catholic pioneer missionary who died in 1835. It owes its modern popularity to a local roadbuilder, 79-year-old Sterling MacKay. In 1991, MacKay says he felt 'driven' to build – at his own expense – a road to the spring. He feels that at least one member of his own family has been helped by the spring, a granddaughter whose *spina bifida* has not been as severe as might be expected. Various unusual properties are claimed for the water. Doyle says that one comes to 'crave' the water: "When you get up in the morning, you want a glass of it. It's a funny thing." A local boatbuilder, John MacEachern, maintains that the water can be kept for years without losing its taste. Ray Coffin, who works for the local fisheries department, said: "It's lovely water. It's not hard, and there are no agricultural contaminants." He is, however, adamant that there is nothing special about it.

IT SEEMS that it's not just water that's good for you – soil can be too. Geophagy – the habit of eating soil – is considered by most modern health professionals to be a symptom of mental illness, but it has a long historical pedigree. The Romans made medicinal tablets from soil mixed with goat's blood. In the 19th century, Germans substituted fine clay for butter on bread. In some African countries, clay is still sold as a digestive remedy; indeed, the kaolin part of the popular diarrhœa remedy kaolin and morphine is simply china clay. Toronto researchers Susan Aufreiter and William Mahaney carried out a scientific investigation of geophagy to see if it did, in fact have health benefits. They tested three samples – yellow soil from Hunan, China, used as 'famine food', clay from Stokes County, North Carolina, said to be a good general tonic, and red soil from termite mounds in Zimbabwe, supposedly good for stomach upsets. The Chinese soil was rich in minerals which would otherwise be in short supply during a famine, the North Carolina clay had significant amounts of iron and iodine, both vital nutrients, and the Zimbabwean soil contained kaolinite, used in commercial diarrhœa treatments.

EVEN regular medicines sometimes find unorthodox uses. Keith Isaacs, a pharmacist at Cairds chemist in Forfar, Scotland, told the National Pharmaceuticals Association about a novel use for anti-pile ointment which a customer had revealed to him. Apparently it can be used to reduce facial wrinkles and bags under the eyes. The cosmetic use of the substance reputedly began with supermodels, but Mr Isaacs warned "Some of these preparations contain hydrocortisone... If you use hydrocortisone, it thins the skin. It may be used by supermodels, who have a limited shelf life, but it is not recommended for the general public."

IT DOESN'T even have to be human medicine. Norwegian Britt Jensen cured herself of crippling back pain by taking her dog's medicine. After putting herself on a course of Fit For Life dog tonic, she made a rapid recovery and as a result the makers Argyll, at Redhill near Bristol, have had to take on extra staff to cope with the flood of orders from hopeful Scandinavians who want to try the cure themselves.

IT DOESN'T EVEN have to be a medicine. A whole range of foodstuffs have been credited with bringing about amazing cures. Marmite has a cult following among bald people, especially in the north of England, a fact discovered by researcher Jonathan Langley who carryied out a study of urban myths and legends. "Appreciable and sometimes spectacular regrowth is said to result when Marmite is liberally and regularly applied to balding heads and left overnight," he said in a letter to

Marketing Week magazine. He also said that converts are easily recognised by their "curiously coloured ebony hair and pervasive odour," but added: "As with all classic urban myths, there is naturally not a hair of corroborative evidence to substantiate this highly dubious story." A spokesman for manufacturers CPC UK Ltd, of Esher, Surrey, said the company would be delighted if the hair treatment actually worked, but concluded: "We would much rather people spread Marmite on their bread."

IN LUGAZI, Uganda, the cure-all of choice is Guinness. Several people claimed it worked miracles for their health, dubbing it *omululuzza* after a local herb used to treat malaria. Many people in the area no longer go to hospital to have fevers treated, as they reckon a single bottle of Guinness is enough to put you back on your feet in hours. At one bar, the owner said people were buying large amounts of Guinness and pouring it into large containers to carry home for the sick, but doctors at Kawolo Hospital dismissed the practice. Dr Isabirye said that people who used Guinness as a medicine were committing suicide, as it didn't contain any antibiotics. He advised them to seek proper medical attention rather than just getting drunk as a 'cure' for their afflictions.

IN ROME, Alfonso Riminni was arrested for selling fake cough mixture and fined £480 by the court. This led to outrage from more than 150 people, who swore Riminni's treatment had worked, even though it was only cabbage water.

UNBELIEVABLE!

Medicine is the home of the inexplicable, with all sorts of amazing recoveries hailed by the church and others as 'miraculous'

AN ASTOUNDING STORY was recounted in the *British Medical Journal* in December 1997. A woman with no history of psychological problems, referred to as AB, heard a voice while she sat at home reading. It told her not to be afraid and said it, and a friend, wanted to help her. She sought medical help and Ikechukwu Azuonye, a consultant psychiatrist who treated the woman, said she appeared to be cured after receiving counselling and medication. The phenomenon recurred while she was on holiday. This time, two voices told her to return to England immediately because there was something wrong with her. Back in London, the address they told her to go to turned out to be the brain scan department of a large London hospital. Mr Azuonye, from the adult mental health unit of Lambeth Healthcare NHS Trust, London, said: "As she arrived, the voices told her to go in and ask to have a brain scan for two reasons – she had a tumour in her brain and her brain stem was inflamed." To reassure her, Mr Azuonye arranged for a scan, even though there was no sign of her having a tumour. He was criticised by colleagues for pandering to her delusions, but the results showed that she did indeed have a tumour. After the operation, AB reported hearing the voices again. This time they told her: "We are pleased to have helped you. Goodbye." She has since made a full recovery.

A 13-YEAR-OLD GIRL in Springfield, Massachusetts, is under consideration for canonisation by the Church. Audrey Santo went into a coma after an accident when she was three. Doctors say she is in a permanent vegetative state. She breathes on her own, her fingers twitch and her eyes move, but they remain unfocused. She bears the stigmata of the crucifixion: her hands, feet and side ooze blood and the wounds from the crown of thorns appear periodically on her forehead. Every week, crucifixes, Virgin Mary statues, and other artefacts in her room secrete oil, which is collected and used to anoint those seeking a cure. According to the Rev George Joyce, spiritual director to Audrey's parents, all the child's miraculous cures have been independently investigated and videotaped. A rash, similar to ones seen on cancer victims during chemotherapy, once appeared on Audrey's legs for a month. As it faded, a group of mothers who had been praying to her because their children had cancer reported that the children were cured. Sensitive to accusations of trickery, Audrey's parents do not solicit payment, though visitors often donate to the Rev Joyce's Church of Our Lady of Hope.

ANOTHER SEVERELY DISABLED child is credited with a large number of miraculous cures, which continue 36 years after her death. Linda Martel was born on Guernsey on 21

August 1956, with *spina bifida* and water on the brain. By the time of her death on 20 October 1961, she is said to have cured more than 1,000 people, often by the laying on of hands. She 'diagnosed' illness by pointing to parts of the body and telling people: "You hurt here." She could also identify who was alive and who was dead, merely by looking at photographs of people. Her reputation began shortly before her third birthday, when she dispelled her father Roy's migraine headaches simply by touching his forehead. Linda, who never went to school, would talk every day about seeing 'her Jesus' or 'her Lady'. Sometimes her face was 'lit up' during her visions. Her mother Eileen recalls how Linda used to have long conversations at night, although neither she nor her husband, a former tobacco salesman, was ever able to get close enough to the bedroom door to hear what she was saying. The talking would stop just before they got within earshot. Mrs Martel, now 71 and living in St Peter Port, still receives large amounts of mail from people around the world seeking miraculous cures. During Linda's lifetime, she used to send out handkerchiefs which Linda had touched and spoken over, using words that her parents couldn't understand. No money exchanged hands, although some people sent Linda gifts. Today, Mrs Martel has one large pink blanket which was used and touched by Linda. She cuts snippets from this last personal item and sends them to people around the world. Those seeking cures still come to touch the girl's gravestone at St Samson's Church.

PAT ENGLISH, 52, a kitchen assistant from Tyne & Wear, discovered in January 1997 that she had a malignant tumour in her right breast. The breast was removed, but by April the cancer had spread to lymph nodes in her right arm; and by June, despite chemotherapy, it was attacking her liver. She was told she had about three months to live. She made her farewells and planned her funeral. As a devout Catholic, she decided to go to Lourdes, a visit financed with the help of a whip-round at work. She went to the holy shrine in July and again in September. A scan a month later showed no sign of cancer, to the puzzlement of the radiographer, who at first suspected machine error. A few weeks later, on 29 November, Pat's first grandchild was born, the grandchild she had never expected to see. Spontaneous remission of inoperable cancer is extremely rare and it takes several years with no sign of recurrence before the cancer can be thought of as cured. "Each day of life I am granted is a wonderful bonus," said Mrs English.

RATHER LESS SUCCESSFUL at Lourdes was a 130-strong party of Scots pilgrims. Most of them returned feeling considerably worse than when they set out, having been struck down with a virulent flu bug. Father Roddy MacNeill, one of the organisers, said he thought someone took the bug out with them and it spread to the rest of the pilgrims. "All the other nationalities were perfectly healthy – until we had been there a few days," he said. "Not exactly a very good advert for Lourdes is it?"

AN UN-NAMED 50-YEAR-OLD British woman, paralysed from the waist down for many years, was carried into the birthplace of St Mary Goretti, south of Rome, in late November. After an hour of 'ardent prayer', she arose and walked towards the other pilgrims exclaiming: "I can walk! I can walk!" She had been praying at the spot where Mary Goretti, 11, was fatally stabbed in 1902. The girl forgave her killer as she lay dying. Bishop Domenico Pecile, investigating, told the Italian press: "The fact that a woman who was apparently paralysed could walk after praying at the shrine is absolutely true. But we are trying to assess whether it was indeed a miracle."

IT'S NOT JUST HUMANS who are in the miracle cure business, Lazarus the horse cures sick farm animals by kissing them. "He's touched by God," claimed his owner, Iowa farmer Jacob Quince. "He was strangled by the umbilical cord at birth, but next morning, Christmas Day, he was on his feet. He heals horses, elephants and even mice."

IN REYKJAVIK, Iceland, hundreds of pilgrims travelled across the world to converge on a tiny shrine in order to pray to a fossilised mackerel, claiming the dried-up fish cures them of their incapacitating illnesses. The mackerel is an ancient Viking relic unearthed by archæologist Larsen Vingard and placed in a small museum. "The Vikings carried talismans which were blessed by holy men and then used aboard ship to ward off evil spirits and bring good fortune," he explained. "Portions of a crumbling manuscript discovered with the mackerel indicated this was the purpose of this particular fish." Tests revealed it was about 1,000 years old. As to its magical status today, Vingard said: "News of the fish's healing properties began spreading by word of mouth, and now we get visitors seeking comfort nearly every day." In China, an even more humble foodstuff has been working miracles. People were flocking to an ancient monastery to worship an ordinary looking cabbage said to be able to cure people miraculously.

IN FARGO, North Dakota, 10-year-old Duane Ross was cured by a talking Christmas tree. The boy suffered a mental handicap which resulted in him being unable to say anything except a few disjointed phrases. However, while visiting a department store, Duane came upon a Christmas tree wired for sound, allowing a member of staff to talk to passing children through a hidden speaker. Duane was attracted by this and the chatty conifer somehow triggered his ability to converse, allowing him to strike up a conversation with it – and he has been talking in proper sentences ever since.

EQUALLY unlikely-sounding is the case of cerebral palsy victim Heaven Leigh (her real name – honest!), whose mother had been told the child would never stand or walk. Nonetheless, Heaven took her first steps after hearing the song 'Achy Breaky Heart', with the mortifying result that singer Billy Ray Cyrus is now hailed as a miracle-worker.

"MIRACLE OF NAPLES, the disabled have been cured," read the headline in Rome's *Il Messaggero* newspaper after the number of people claiming disability benefits in the city fell from 60,000 to 13,000 in a three-year period. This may well have had something to do with a massive police crackdown on benefit fraud in Naples. Among other anomalies, the police found 40 people claiming disability payments for blindness who could see well enough to drive cars.

MARK BOWKER, 9, of Chalgrove in Oxfordshire, severed a fingertip when it got stuck in a door at school. The fingertip then regrew. Doctors at Oxford's John Radclyffe Hospital said that regeneration is fairly well documented in children of up to about three years old, but had never before occurred in a nine-year-old.

SEVEN YEARS of torment ended for Linda and Howard Johnson when Linda gave birth to their son Todd. They had tried everything, but even fertility treatment failed. However, they read about a pair of ancient ebony statues which were supposed to be responsible for more than 300 unplanned pregnancies. They found the statues in the Blackpool Pleasure Beach branch of Ripley's Believe It Or Not. "I had to touch the baby the female statue was holding, while Howard stroked the spearhead on the male figure," said Linda. "The next minute I felt pins and needles in my hand, and a tingling sensation which travelled up my arm to my elbow." After a steamy sex session that night, Todd was conceived, duly arriving nine months later. The statues, worshipped by the African Baule tribe, make parents of anyone who touches them, according to legend.

AT THE BEGINNING of May 1999, a shaven-headed swarthy man was discovered unconscious at the foot of a staircase in Swindon Railway station, Wiltshire. He had an alien tattoo on his left arm and his holdall was stuffed with books on UFOs and the paranormal. He had a map of Snowdonia and a rail ticket from Swansea to Bristol. A month later he was unidentified and still in a coma.

THE FULL MOON has long been alleged to cause insanity, giving us the term 'lunacy', but an 11-year survey of admission rates at a London psychiatric hospital revealed that there may actually be some truth to the old wives tale. The study, published in *Nursing Times* found that more admissions took place during the full-moon than in any of the other three phases of the lunar cycle. Over the 11 years the average admission rate per lunar cycle should have been 378. During other cycles admissions were between 352 and 366 per cycle, but when there was a full moon they rose to 423.

BUDDHIST HOLY MAN Dawa has baffled doctors by remaining in perfect health without having slept for nearly 80 years. He is awake and cheerfull, holding conversations while his vital signs hover at levels lower than when normal people are sound asleep.

CHAPTER ELEVEN

MEDICAL MISCELLANY

As ever, there are some tales just too odd to fit anywhere else

WHEN THE BEATLES sang of "the girl with kaleidoscope eyes," some medically-minded listeners heard it as "the girl with colitis goes by."

A STUDY by the University of San Diego of 27 years' worth of California death certificates has revealed that a man's initials influence his longevity. Only men were looked at because their initials don't change with marriage. Those with initials like WOW, ACE and GOD tended to live more than seven years longer than those labelled RAT, PIG or DUD.

RETIRED BUSINESSMAN Klaus Schmidt, 64, suffered serious heart problems and had difficulty breathing at 11,000ft on a Lufthansa flight from Dublin to Frankfurt. The chief steward asked if there was a doctor on board and was met with the 40

raised arms of the entire German delegation to an international medical seminar in Ireland. Many were carrying newly-developed heart drugs in their hand luggage. A professor from a heart clinic in Heidelberg loosened Mr Schmidt's collar, while a specialist in microscopic surgery gave him an injection. Within minutes, the colour returned to Mr Schmidt's cheeks, and he was breathing more easily. He was able to walk from the plane with some help. "I was lucky to choose the right flight," he told a stewardess. "I'd been thinking of flying back the next day and then changed my mind."

A WOMAN treated by a passing doctor after a car crash in 1993 met her again after the doctor crashed through her house. Judy Thompson, of Solihull, returned the favour, giving Stella Isaac first aid and calling an ambulance.

YOUNG ADULTS who are attracted to 'New Age' groups or sects may be seeking to cope with the onset of schizophrenia, Dr Jan Libiger, a leading European psychiatrist from the Czech Republic, told colleagues at a media briefing in Geneva recently.

DEXTER GORDON, the tenor and soprano saxophonist, played Dale Turner, a jazz genius struggling against drink and drugs, in Bertrand Tavernier's film *Around Midnight*. During filming, the studio doctors discovered that he had virtually no liver and an astounding level of blood alcohol. At over 150, a driver's licence is automatically forfeited; over 250, one is considered clinically insane. Gordon's alcohol content registered at 1,200.

THE SEVENTH Annual Ig Nobel Prize Ceremony, held before 1,200 people at Harvard University, is a spoof of the Nobel prizes that honours people whose achievements "cannot or should not be reproduced". The prize for medicine was awarded to three American researchers who discovered that the musak played in lifts could stimulate the immune system and "thus help to prevent the common cold". An investigation by Japanese and Czech researchers into brainwave patterns of people who chew different flavours of gum picked up the prize for biology.

IN A SURVEY of aphrodisiacs, red wine came out as the top turn-on, beating white wine, ginseng and champagne. One of the testers said it turned her on for 24 hours. There was no mention of emu eggs in the survey, but Australian artist Ivan Durrant discovered entirely by accident that their shells had aphrodisiac qualities. He was carving patterns into emu eggs and "there was a lot of egg dust flying around. I licked my fingers and, well, I was unstoppable," he said.

DOCTORS should work naked in the operating theatre claims Stockholm surgeon G Turrevall. He reckons "people are carriers of all kinds of bacteria, and theatre staff are no exception. Their gowns rub against their skin, causing the bacteria to brush off. These circulate in the air and may get into the patient's blood during surgery."

HOWEVER, we doubt naked theatre staff would appreciate the experience surgeon Jonathan Earnshaw had while operating at the City Hospital, Nottingham. While operating on a man with stomach cancer, they made an incision using an instrument which heats the tissue with an electric current. The moment the stomach opened, the gases inside ignited and exploded, spattering a nurse and medical equipment with the contents of the patient's stomach, which the team had been unable to suck out completely due to a blockage. Earnshaw could not find any signs of damage, and after the operation, the patient made an uneventful recovery.

IN MICHIGAN, a psoriasis sufferer undergoing tar, steroid and ultraviolet light treatments for the skin ailment burst into flames when he lit a cigarette. Fortunately, he wasn't badly hurt.

A DOSE of suntan pills turned Lorraine Foster, of Cheltenham, Gloucestershire, bright orange. They contained enough vitamin A for 12,000 carrots. After this and other incidents, the manufacturers dropped vitamin A from the Bronztan tablets.

ACCORDING to researchers at Wageningen Agricultural University in Holland, people with smelly feet are more likely to be attacked by mosquitoes. Research student Bart Knols sat under a mosquito net in his underpants while mosquitoes were released. Three quarters of them headed for his feet.

THE OWNER of a roller-skating cockatoo received $2,000 in compensation after the bird had to be put down, along with three million others, in order to halt the spread of an epidemic of highly contagious Newcastle Disease. "Before we euthenised him, we had him roller skate one last time," said an appraiser involved in the project, "then we gassed him."

A MAN walked backwards round Indonesia after promising his doctor he would if cured of a crippling ailment. Treatment worked, so off he went...

A JUDGE in Fresno, California, spared a boy with a club foot from surgery because of his family's fear of arousing evil spirits which could kill him. A psychiatrist told judge Lawrence O'Neill that the trauma of going against traditional Hmong beliefs by allowing surgery could also kill members of Kou Xiong's family, refugees from Laos.

KARL FALKENHAINER, from San Francisco, was arrested by police after he cut off a friend's paralysed foot with a chainsaw. Police said Falkenhainer and his friend, Philip St Pierre, 30, agreed the foot should be amputated, so they went out and bought a chainsaw to do the job. Police did not take such a liberal view of things, and charged Falkenhainer with causing mayhem and assault.

A STUDY of dental patients revealed that for many the experience of losing their teeth was on a par with having a hysterectomy or losing a limb, according to a report in the *British Dental Journal*. One woman told researchers how she kept bursting into tears after some of her lower teeth were taken out and another interviewee said: "I could have spoken openly to someone about the death of a friend but not the death of my teeth. People have died that I have loved... you can get over it. But this grief is inside me and it's private and it's very personal and that's why, even after all these years, I feel cheated."

IN SEATTLE, David Powell slept his way into the *Guinness Book of Records* with the longest dream ever recorded – three hours. Powell, a patient at the Puget Sound Sleep Disorder Centre in Seattle was recorded in a dream state, characterised by rapid eye movement (REM) for three hours and eight minutes. He comprehensively beat the old record of two hours and 23 minutes. Powell was at the centre being treated for obstructive sleep apnœa, which stops the patient breathing during the night, preventing them getting any REM sleep. Normally, people experience an REM phase every 90 minutes or so while sleeping, and these last 15–30 minutes at a time. As part of his treatment, Powell was fitted with a mask which blows a continuous stream of air in to the nasal passage, keeping the airway open and allowing the patient to fall into a deep sleep. He hadn't been able to get any REM sleep for 10 or 15 years, so when fitted with the mask, he experienced a massive REM 'rebound', leading to the record-breaking dream. When he was asked later what he had been dreaming about, Boeing worker Powell said he was dreaming about flying a fighter jet.

IT'S A COCK-UP

We don't want to alarm anybody, but it's amazing how many cases of medical negligence we have on file – and these are just the unusual ones!

A SOUTH KOREAN woman aged 38 was strapped into a barrel-like magnetic resolution imaging (MRI) machine in a Seoul hospital for a scan of her neck. A technician passed the film to the surgical department, and left for a four-day public holiday, forgetting about the patient. The terrified woman was trapped in the sealed and pitch-dark scanner chamber for 29 hours before freeing herself the following night. How is not explained.

AN ARGENTINIAN with no medical degree worked as a neurologist in a top hospital for 16 years, chaired a specialist conference and co-wrote a book on medicine. Guillermo Assaneo was "a great seducer with the gift of the gab," said one doctor at the Rivadavia Hospital in Buenos Aires, where Assaneo, 48, worked from 1972 to 1988. His imposture was discovered after a woman told police she had suffered permanent brain damage in an operation he had recommended. Following a road accident, Susan Farmer, an Army corporal based in Germany, was given a saline drip at the crash scene. She later discovered that her rescuer had no medical qualifications and had arrived in a private car with blue flashing lights. The drip could have exacerbated a brain hæmorrhage.

NADINE COOL, of Wisconsin, is suing her psychiatrist Dr Kenneth Olson for malpractice, claiming he convinced her she had 120 personalities (including Satan, angels who talked to God, and a duck), and then charged her insurance company $300,000 for group therapy.

FOR FOUR WEEKS after a brain tumour operation in June, retired teacher Goran Rudolfsson sneezed his way round the town of Hoverberg on Sweden's west coast with his sinuses blocked and head buzzing. On 11 July, he felt something move inside his nostril and spent half an hour pulling out a swab from inside his head. It was 31in long and an inch wide. "Fortunately, no harm seems to have been done," said a spokeswoman for Umea University Hospital, where the operation had been performed. "We have apologised to Mr Rudolfsson and thanked him for returning the swab to us. He had washed and ironed it." Other objects discovered inside people include a four-inch-long plastic tube abandoned in the stomach of an Indian man, J Mehra, for 25 years; and a 2.8in gauze swab left inside the stomach of Italian mother Giuditta Consonni, 55, after she had her first child by Cæsarean section 25 years previously. A Colombian man who reported abdominal pains, discovered that he had been living with a pair of surgical forceps in his stomach for 47 years. Silvio Jimenez was a

20-year-old army conscript back in 1950 when he was stabbed at a party and rushed to the Valledupar regional hospital, 546 miles north of Bogota. "The doctor who operated on him at that time forgot one of his tools inside his patient," said Rafael Zabaleta, the Valledupar doctor who removed the forceps.

IN SWEDEN, a 63-year-old man had to be taken to hospital for X-rays after a dentist fixing a bridge in the man's mouth dropped a 3cm long screwdriver down his throat. The X-rays showed the tool in his gullet, and later check-ups showed it had moved to his stomach. The screwdriver came out 'the natural way'. It is not known whether the dentist got it back, but apparently he now always ties the screwdriver to his thumb when doing similar dental bridge work.

ABDEL-SATTAR ABDEL-SALEM BADAWI, a chauffeur in his 60s, suffering from fibrosis of the liver, was pronounced dead in a hospital in the Nile delta city of Menoufia, 65 miles northwest of Cairo. He was put in a morgue refrigerator. Revived by the cold, he awoke from a coma after 12 hours, slid open the coffin lid and began chanting verses from the Koran and shouting for help. No-one heard, but then three hospital orderlies came in to remove his body and found him standing up. One of them fell dead from shock. Mr Badawi vowed never again to go to hospital.

IN MILAN, nurse Antonio Busnelli, 40, was jailed for 28 years after he was found guilty of giving two patients lethal injections so that he could earn extra cash moonlighting as a hearse driver.

ELSEWHERE, in Rotterdam, a trainee surgeon was fired after roaring through the lobby of a hospital on a Harley-

Davidson motorcycle, then taking it up in a lift and hurtling through an intensive care ward.

A KENYAN DOCTOR at a clinic north of Nairobi removed a bean that Jacqueline Wambui, six, had accidentally stuck in her ear while playing. He demanded £3.50, but the girl's father, Stephan Muchina, offered the £2.70 he had on him and asked to pay 80p later. The doctor refused and pushed the bean back in the girl's ear. Mr Muchina reported the incident to the local police station, and the doctor was arrested on unspecified charges.

THIRTEEN DAYS after surgeons removed her cancerous bladder in a Richmond, Virginia, hospital, Virginia Broache discovered she had carried the organ home in her overnight bag. A home nurse found it wrapped in a surgical towel and sealed in a double plastic bag.

HOSPITAL WORKER Dorothy Dunn, 48, was sacked from Tameside General Hospital in Greater Manchester for taking three months off sick – after being wrongly told she had angina by the same hospital.

FRANK AXFORD, 76, got more than he bargained for when he went into Treliske Hospital, Truro, Cornwall, to be treated for cancer of the colon. The doctor set his bottom on fire. "It seems I went up like a Christmas pudding," Axford said. He was under general anæsthetic and was unaware that the accident had happened, but when he came round, doctors explained that there'd been an accident and that a spirit-based fluid had been ignited with an electric cauterising gun used in the operation. The cancer surgery was successful, but two months later he still couldn't sit down comfortably. "I did not feel anything for about two or three days, and then it started to hurt," Mr Axford complained "It was more painful than the operation. There are two big circles where I was burnt. It is not very funny." The hospital sent him a special cushion and a nurse visited every day, but Mr Axford was still taking legal advice.

A FEDERAL JURY in Alexandria, Virginia, convicted sperm bank operator Dr Cecil Jacobson on 52 charges of fraud after it was discovered that he had been inseminating women with his own sperm while claiming to use other donors. Assistant US Attorney Randy Bellows said that Jacobson had fathered more than 70 children with couples in the area. "I have spent my life trying to help women have children," Jacobson said after the decision was read. "It's a shock to be found guilty of trying to help people." He insisted he had not broken any law, but faced up to 280 years in prison and fines of up to £250,000.

AN ASSISTANT MEDICAL EXAMINER in Stamford, Connecticut, found a medical training doll seen on a darkened roadside all too realistic and declared it dead. Henry Minot mistook the doll for an aborted, partially frozen fœtus, and sent it to the Chief Medical Examiner for an autopsy. Police found the doll after a passerby called them. It was covered in sand and gravel and one of its arms was severed.

BRAIN SURGERY is a high enough risk activity without the doctors making it any worse. In Saskatoon, Canada, the operating tables in the Royal University Hospital became so wobbly that staff had to prop them up with stools to keep them from moving while brain surgery was carried out. And in New York, state officials were investigating a $1,000,000 claim made by a 54-year-old woman who alleged that a hospital in Watertown lost a six-inch portion of her skull during brain surgery. Elsewhere, a neurosurgeon's license was suspended after it was found that he went off to lunch in mid-operation, leaving the patient's brain exposed for 25 minutes. Dr Raymond Sattler also forgot the names of surgical equipment during operations, told a nurse to drill holes in a patient's head and work on the outer brain, though she was not trained to do so, and ordered intravenous fluids to be given to him during an operation to prevent him passing out.

IN WALES, hospital authorities launched a probe after a patient fell ill following a St David's Day meal which contained a daffodil. A member of staff at Swansea's Cefn Coed Hospital was suspended after the incident.

IN TAMPA, FLORIDA, police found three tons of soiled bandages, used hypodermic needles, teeth, and other biohazard material at the home of a medical waste haulier named Gary Barlow (so that's what he did when his solo career went pear-shaped...), which took five trucks to remove. Officials found 6,447lb of hazardous waste stashed in boxes and the red disposal bags used for medical waste strewn throughout his house, which was not licensed as a biohazard containment facility. Barlow gave no explanation for his unsanitary stash.

WEDDING TACKLE

A remarkable number of medical tales seem to relate
some sort of ghastly occurrence involving male genitalia –
we wonder why?

THE FEAR of vanishing family jewels wafted around West
Africa throughout 1997. In late July and early August, lynch
mobs in Senegal burned and beat to death at least eight alleged
sorcerers (all from other African countries) suspected of having
the power to make a penis vanish or shrink with a mere hand-
shake. More than 30 other people were seriously injured.
Papers in Dakar published pictures of suspected 'genital
thieves' killed by angry crowds and *Le Matin* asked in a banner
headline: "Have we lost our common sense?" Three of the
deaths were in Dakar, and *Le Soleil* reported that five people
from Niger had been killed by mobs in Ziguinghor, southern
Casamance province.

FOLLOWING the penis-snatching panics in West Africa,
herbal doctor Abe Owerri was arrested in Nigeria and charged

with obtaining money under false pretences. His tactic was to approach someone on the street, shake him by the hand and then throw himself to the ground screaming that his penis had vanished. With his victim transfixed with astonishment, the doctor's accomplices would step in and mug him. The no-penis defence may be compromised in court when it emerges that many of these accomplices were among the doctor's 144 children. In mid-June, the shrinking panic had spread to Gabon. A crowd in Libreville beat up a Malian accused of making another chap's wedding tackle vanish.

IF YOUR WEDDING TACKLE does vanish, it now seems you are not beyond medical help, as penis transplants are now a reality, or at least that's how it seems. In 1987, Thai doctors claimed the world's first successful penis transplant, when the organ of a person undergoing a sex-change operation was sewn onto a soldier whose own todger had been cut off by his jealous wife. Bangkok surgeons said it was a coincidence that Private Kovit Bamrungna came in at the same time as someone was waiting to have his penis removed, allowing them to swap the organ from someone who didn't want it to someone who did. The news does not seem to have reached leading Italian plastic surgeon Professor Nicolo Scuderi, though. He was still speculating whether the operation might be possible as late as 1998, and had three patients lined up to be 'the first' to receive a transplant. He'd also clearly missed out on another Thai case in 1995, when a penis transplant recipient sued the surgeon because his new one was two inches shorter than the one he'd lost, and an extremely unlikely-sounding operation supposedly carried out in China in 1993. According to a report from the New China News Agency, a husband and his wife swapped genitalia in a 19-hour operation, with the husband, Wang (!), 30, becoming the wife and his wife, Hou, 24, going the other way. "The previous male, now a female, has obtained a fine skin, shapely body and gentle temper, while the previous female has grown a pale moustache and adopted a bold and unconstrained character," the report claimed.

VANITY can be a terrible thing. Public health officials in Thailand warned men not to try to have their penises enlarged after three men needed theirs amputated after quack doctors injected them with a mixture of chalk powder and olive oil to achieve the longed-for dimensions. In Berlin, a man who had paid £5,000 for enlargement surgery sued the hospital when he emerged with a penis smaller than the one he arrived with. Elsewhere, the world record for penis extension is held by Copenhagen plastic surgeon Joern Ege Siana. By a combination of surgery and post-surgery stretching, he lengthened a 42-year-old's flaccid member from 4.5cm to 19cm.

IN TOULOUSE, France, a hospital cock-up meant that Marcel Danielou, 51, in hospital for surgery on his bunions, was sent to the wrong operating theatre and received a large mechanical penis extension instead. He didn't complain. In Recife, Brazil, the recipient of a mechanical penis implant refused to pay for it, as it operated every time his neighbours used their television remotes.

ALL THIS effort might have been in vain though. Hunter Wessels and Jack McAninch (an appropriate name for the task!) carried out a survey of 60 men to discover the average penis size. They injected 60 men with a drug which causes erections, then measured the results, concluding that the average erect penis is 5in long. They carried out their research in order to help doctors decide whether patients coming to them for penis enlargements really needed an operation. On the other hand, another scientist, Louise Guillette claims that chemical pollution is having a terrible effect on the male genitals. She reckons the decline in the male sex hormone testosterone has led to considerable shrinkage. "The manhood of modern men is only half the size of their grandfathers," she said. It's not just us either; research in Florida has shown alligator penises are getting shorter too. The good news is, though, that tight-fitting underpants, long thought to reduce fertility, do no such thing, according to a year-long study of 21 Californian men.

FORESKINS, though, *are* getting much bigger – up to the size of six football pitches! Scientists seeking new ways to treat burns victims, have found that they can use the foreskins removed at circumcision to grow large sheets of skin which can then be grafted over burnt areas. In the laboratory, one single foreskin can be persuaded to grow enough skin to cover those six football pitches.

IF you actually want to find out how big someone's tackle is without forcing them to drop their Calvins, the old wives' tale about men's hands and feet being a good indicator has been shown to be true. Biologists in Geneva investigating limb development in mice bred a strain without a gene that is vital for the process. They found that without it, the mice grew without fingers, toes or penises, and varying amounts of the gene dictated the size of these parts. The more of the gene they carried, the longer their fingers and toes – and their penises – were.

AN 82-YEAR-OLD MAN with waterworks problems regularly used a haricot bean as a plug. The bean got stuck, and he couldn't get it out with tweezers. Three days later, it started sprouting, and he ended up in Southend General Hospital having it removed with forceps under general anæsthetic, according to an article written by Dr Anup Patel in the *British Medical Journal*.

BRIAN PELLOW, a farm hand in South Wales, was awarded £250,000 for the loss of his sex life after he was attacked and injured by a huge pig. Pellow was trying to put a collar on the sow when she went berserk and knocked him off his feet. The pain from the back injuries he received prevented him from having sex again. "This pig was no Babe, this was one nasty pig," Pellow's lawyer told the court.

ALSO SUING for loss of nookie was computer operator Simon Wadmore, 42. He sued the government after he fell off his 100-year-old penny farthing bike when grooves in the poorly-maintained road forced him into the path of oncoming traffic, where he collided with a car. The car ran him over, causing multiple injuries including a crushed backbone, broken pelvis, cracked ribs, and kidney damage. It also forced his genitals into contact with the hot exhaust pipe, burning his manhood seriously, after which he could not make love to his wife, Ann, normally.

IAN MARSHALL, an air force officer from Cheltenham, was awarded £3,000 compensation after a kick in the groin from fellow officer Alan Udolloress during a rugby match gave him a constant erection for more than a week, a condition known as priapism. He was told he had a damaged urethra and to treat the persistent tumescence with ice packs. Even so, the swelling still took three days to deflate. Udolloress was found guilty of actual bodily harm, but explained he had been trying to kick the ball. Rather more surprising was the case of priapism suffered by a patient of urologist Irwin Goldstein: the sufferer was female! She was taking the antidepressant Trazone, but a few days after the course began, her clitoris swelled painfully and permanently. Goldstein treated her with a drug known to reduce priapism in men, and within a day the swelling subsided, but the case went down in the records as the first instance of drug-induced female priapism.

ANOTHER appropriate named victim of todger trauma was Dean Askew, who was unable to indulge in traditional wedding night activities after he snapped his penis five days before his marriage was to take place. "I woke up with what is often called 'morning glory', rolled over and heard a noise like a bone snapping," Dean said. "A shooting pain went up my old man, and it swelled to the size of an orange." He was rushed to hospital, where doctors found he had ruptured a vein. They said they would have to operate immediately or he'd never perform again. Dean received 20 stitches and only got out of hospital 24 hours before the ceremony. He was so heavily bandaged that he had to wear baggy trousers. After probably the least romantic wedding-night ever, Dean and his new wife had to wait months before they had any chance of consummating their relationship.

WHILE Dean Askew's injury might have sounded like a bone snapping, for a 57-year-old Italian man, the possibility of such an injury was all too real. On visiting the doctors for help with a painfully curving erection in which he thought he could feel a thick mass, he found he had the boner to end all boners. X-rays revealed he had a 2.5in long U-shaped piece of bone running down the back of his penis and looping up the front, surrounding the left erectile body. Doctors couldn't remove the bone, so were forced to fracture it and operate to reduce the curvature. While chimp and gorilla penises contain a bone, human ones do not, and experts were stumped as to what could have caused this rare formation. They suggested that scar tissue had probably started the process, with constant stimulation encouraging the change from skin to bone.

A CHINESE INVENTOR has come up with a new form of male contraceptive. The pocket-sized device is worn inside the underwear and emits pulses which affect nerves in a man's body, rendering him temporarily sterile. Fertility returns if the device is not used for two months. The device, developed in the city of Xi'an is described as "convenient, safe and reliable."

A WARWICKSHIRE WOMAN became pregnant with twins after dashing to a fertility clinic with her husband's testicle in a coffee flask. The husband had undergone emergency surgery to have his remaining testicle removed after a diagnosis of cancer. With no time to donate sperm before the operation it had been decided to extract the testicle and take it to a clinic where sperm could be removed and frozen.

The main problem was keeping the excised teste at body temperature during the hour-and-a-half drive. "I am sure there are more appropriate methods of transporting tissues around, but the coffee flask worked as well as anything else," said clinic spokeswoman Anna Kavanagh. Presumably the coffee was emptied out first.

AFTER A SOLDIER underwent a revolutionary penis lengthening procedure in a Dutch military hospital, authorities were not impressed. The soldier had 4cm added to his penis by having the internal segment detached from the pubic bone, allowing the portion normally concealed within the abdomen to be exposed. Abdominal skin was then grafted onto the exposed section. This apparently doubled its length.

However, hospital spokesman, Derk van't Spijker said "This is not a normal operation in Holland. As long as it's not a normal operation it won't be done in a military hospital. It was the first and last time."

RADICAL SURGERY

Extreme problems sometimes require extreme solutions

BRIDGET FUDGELL suffers from *ankylosing spondylitis*, which fuses vertebræ together. After she broke her neck in 1993, her head became fixed in a downward position, looking slightly to the right. "I couldn't see to cross the road," she said. She was told that nothing could be done and resigned herself to a lifetime of pain, immobility and depression. In a 17-hour operation, neurosurgeon Steve Gill, of the Frenchay Hospital, Bristol, detached her head from her spinal column, leaving it connected by just the spinal cord, key blood vessels and the skin at the front of her neck. He then cut a 30 degree wedge out of the base of her skull and the top vertebra before fixing her head back with a metal plate and two screws, leaving her looking forward. "There comes a point where the head is loose relative to the neck and you have to start manœuvring the neck around, avoiding any pressure on any of these structures. That is quite a precarious time," said Gill, who presented the case to the British Society of Neurosurgeons. Mr Gill had carried out radical surgery before. In 1995, he drilled a hole in the head of a man suffering from Parkinson's disease – while the patient was awake – to implant an electrode.

ON 16 SEPTEMBER 1997, an unnamed 28-year-old woman's face and scalp were ripped off after her hair caught in a milking machine on her farm in Victoria, Australia, leaving only her chin and one ear intact. Her face and scalp were packed in ice and taken with her to St Vincent's Hospital, Melbourne, where two teams of surgeons under Prof Wayne Morrison, one of the world's leading plastic surgeons, replaced her features. "What we saw was a head that essentially looked like what you see in an anatomical dissection," said Prof Morrison. Using microscopes, they reattached blood vessels and nerves. During the 25-hour operation, the woman was given 30 units of blood, almost double the body's eight pints. Six days later, she was still in intensive care, but Morrison said he was 'fairly confident' that her face would look much the same as before the accident. Once the graft had taken and the blood supply had been re-established, the biggest problem would be to restore feeling to the face. He admitted there were still formidable problems of tissue rejection to overcome, but said: "This is a dry run for actually transplanting faces. This is what we could only dream we could do." He knew of only one comparable operation performed before, several years ago in China.

THREE-YEAR-OLD Megan McFarlane was eating an ice-cream in Arbroath when a 100lb bull mastiff leapt up and bit her on the face, tearing off her top lip. When ambulancemen could not find the missing lip, they realised that the dog must have swallowed it. Fortunately, the dog's owner realised the gravity of the situation and suggested that the dog be taken to a vet, put down, and its stomach searched for the missing lip. John Keen, the vet who carried out the task, said it had been difficult to find the lip inside the dog, but once he had done so, he placed it in a mixture of ice and saline. The rescued part was then rushed to Dundee Royal Infirmary, arriving only five minutes after the girl, to whom it was re-attached. Anas Naasan, the surgeon who carried out the operation, explained: "The dog had not chewed the lip, otherwise the operation would have been impossible, though the edges were a bit crushed. We were also concerned about bacteria, so the tissue was cleaned with antiseptic and the girl was given antibiotics as a precaution against infection." The operation is believed to be the first one in which tissue was re-attached after recovery from the stomach of an animal.

BRITISH DOCTOR Steve Hindley, 42, had been practising as a 'bush locum' in Ravensthorpe, Western Australia, for just a day when Hayden McGlinn collapsed after a sporting accident. Emergency neuro-surgery was needed to relieve pressure from a blood clot on the brain, but Hindley realised that the sportsman was unlikely to survive until the Flying Doctor service arrived.

A specialist in the Charles Gairdner Hospital in Perth, 600 miles away, advised over the phone that the pressure should be relieved by boring a hole in the man's left temple. The Ravensthorpe cottage hospital, where Dr Hindley was the only doctor, had nothing suitable and a dentist's drill proved useless. Finally, a rusting brace and bit was found in a school shed, and Dr Hindley performed the 15-minute procedure once the tool had been cleaned and sterilised. The pressure on the brain was relieved and the patient flown to hospital, where he slowly recovered. The brace and bit was mounted in a display case in Ravensthorpe's only pub.

PROFESSOR Andrew Wallace of Queen's Medical Centre, Nottingham, who performed life-saving surgery in an æroplane, received the $50,000 Weigelt Wallace prize for extraordinary dedication to medicine. He was aboard a British Airways Boeing 707 travelling to London from Hong Kong on 22 May, 1995, when passenger Pauline Dixon, 39, complained of chest pains. Dixon, who had been involved in a motorbike crash on the way to the airport, had fractured ribs and a collapsed lung. BA offered to land at New Delhi, but Wallace feared the change in cabin pressure could be fatal. With the aid of Dr Tom Wong, from Tayside, he took a scalpel and local anæsthetic from the aircraft's emergency kit and cut into Dixon's chest. Dr Wong held the wound open with a knife and fork sterilised in five-star brandy. Wallace inserted a chest drain made from a urinary catheter (also sterilised in brandy), strengthened with a coathanger and held in place with adhesive tape. The air pocket on her left lung was drained out through a mineral water bottle adapted as a one-way valve. The 10-minute operation was successful, and by the time Flight 32 landed 12 hours later, Dixon was well enough for breakfast.

USING ONLY some scissors and a mirror, an American woman removed her own tonsils. She took the surgery into her own hands after finding she was unable to pay for the operation. She cut the tonsils away bit by bit over a few weeks. The amateur surgery was apparently a complete success.

ALSO finding he was a bit short of cash for a medical procedure was Swedish restaurant owner Ridha Bouhlal. He was forced to subsist on soup for four months after his dentist discovered he could not pay for work he had done and forcibly removed the dental implants he had installed, leaving Mr Bouhlal with no teeth in his lower jaw, only a titanium screw.

IF THIS had been Norma Wickwire, a 76-year-old grandmother from Inverness, Florida, there might have been real problems. Since 1976 doctors have replaced eight of her 10 major joints with artificial ones. She has had both hips, both knees, both shoulders, an ankle and an elbow replaced, earning her the nickname 'The Bionic Grandma' and a place in the *Guinness Book of Records* under the heading 'Medical Extremes'.

A GROUP of Latvian surgeons were after an entry in the *Guinness Book of Records*. They hoped to get in after reattaching four severed hands in five days, which they reckoned was a world record. In case you were wondering whether they had cut them off specially to go for the record, it seems the answer is no. Three of the patients had their hands cut off by saws while chopping down trees, while the fourth was a woman whose hand was wrenched off by a dough machine. According to the Baltic News Service, the doctors usually reattached only two or three hands a year.

IN MOROCCO, a badly burned girl was saved when surgeons wrapped her in the skin of a wild boar. 10-year-old Loubna Meshour was seriously injured in an explosion at her home when the gas cooker blew up and would have died, but a visiting Chinese medical team used the boar skin as a protective dressing while they carried out a series of skin grafts to save her life.

IN HOUSTON, Texas, surgeons removed Gary Altmann's heart to cut away a lemon-sized tumour. They then rebuilt the damaged organ with pig and cow tissue, and re-implanted it. At the time the story was published, the hospital was refusing to comment on the 20-year-old student's condition.

INDONESIAN DOCTORS removed a tumour weighing 35kg from a woman in Eastern Java. They took two hours to extract the massive growth from Maimunah, 20, at a hospital in the Probolinggo district. She had had the tumour for four years, but had been afraid of having surgery.

QUEUES of people formed at the Holy Heart hospital in Belgium in order to view a giant gallstone. The apple-sized stone weighing 507g was extracted from a local pensioner at the hospital. They could only put it on show for a short while. The pensioner wanted it back to use as a conversation piece in his home.

CHAPTER FIFTEEN

BACK FROM THE DEAD

Death, the final curtain... or not

IN NOVEMBER 1977, Swami Satya Moorthi, who claimed to be 102 years old, had sensors attached to his body and assumed a meditative position. He was put into an eight-foot square box six feet underground, which was bricked up, and Dr Y G Mathur settled down in a monitoring van. After 15 minutes, the Swami's pulse fell to 68 beats per minute and his temperature to 80.6 degrees Fahrenheit. On day two, his pulse raced to 178 beats and then stopped.

The cardiogram showed no signs of life for seven days, and police arrived to dig up the yogi, and arrest and charge the medics. They were persuaded to leave, and the experiment continued for a further 192 hours, after which the yogi was dug up; he emerged in good condition. Mathur explained that it was "man's answer to hibernation" and the Swami's way of extending his life on Earth.

ALLISON BURCHELL 57, suffers from cataplexy, a bizarre disease which leaves her apparently dead when her pulse becomes impossible to detect. Her condition was diagnosed in 1951, when she was 16, and she was monitored in hospital for a year. Since then, she has been declared dead at least six times. Once, she woke up freezing on a mortuary slab. She asked the attendant to take her back to her room, but he screamed and bolted. Her attacks can be brought on by any sudden fright, shock or even laughter. By February 1989, she was taking a 'life drug', and had not had an attack for nearly six years; as a young woman, she had had up to two or three a week. She moved from Surrey to Melbourne, Australia, where she worked as a computer operator. After she described her condition in a newspaper, she was fired by her employers.

GEORGE BARR, 82, complained of chest pains on 30 March, 1990 and had a massive heart attack. He failed to respond to half an hour of emergency treatment with drugs, cardiopulmonary massage, electric shock therapy and a respirator. Thirteen minutes after being pronounced dead, Barr began breathing again. Dr Sheldon H Gottleib, of Johns Hopkins University in Baltimore, explained that a primitive reflex sometimes allows the body to use oxygen saved by virtually shutting down all other body systems. Barr was comatose for a day, then woke up with a craving for chow mein. He was released from hospital a month later, and died in his sleep of a heart attack on 20 February 1992.

DURING A FUNERAL service in Longano, northern Italy, the 'deceased', Ernest Quirino, 60, opened his eyes, looked round in horror, leapt out of the coffin and ran. He collapsed after about 100 yards, but a doctor said later that he was well.

GERRY ALLISON was in a hearse on the way to his own funeral when a tyre burst and his coffin was flung out of the hearse and into the window of a rival undertaker's parlour. Allison, dressed in white robes, stepped out through the shattered glass, having been roused from a coma which doctors had mistaken for death.

AN 18-YEAR-OLD Romanian girl, declared clinically dead, regained consciousness while being raped on a slab by a Bucharest mortuary attendant. Police arrested the shocked rapist, but the parents refused to press charges because their daughter "owed her life to him."

IN NAMUR, Belgium, a teenager returned from the dead as her family prepared to bury her. Ten days after 19-year-old waitress Delphine Barbiaux vanished from her home, police found a girl's battered body lying in a ditch. They called Delphine's mother, who positively identified the corpse. However, as friends and family gathered round her coffin to mourn, the girl rang home to say she was alive and had been staying with friends. She had seen reports of her death in the paper and realised there had been a mistake. At the time the reports were written, police had no idea who the corpse was.

A SIMILAR mistake was made in the case of Michael Kirby, who had lost contact with his family, when police dragged a body from the Thames. After the corpse was identified as his by a cousin who had viewed photographs of the remains, it was shipped home to Kyle, in Tipperary, and given a tearful burial. Four months later, however, his daughter Mary spotted him, alive and well, at Victoria station, and, deeply shocked, took him to her home in Poplar, south London, before notifying relatives and the police. Kirby had set out from Tipperary over a year before to visit his sister Kathy in London, but had lost his memory *en route* and never arrived. He had been living rough and in a hostel at Westminster Cathedral ever since. Police, though, were left with the puzzle of working out who exactly had been buried in Michael's grave in Ireland.

WHILE Kirby's return from the dead had a happy ending, Madiha el-Sayed's was rather more fraught. The 40-year-old housemaid was due to sail on a ferry which struck a coral reef in the Red Sea and sank, leaving 484 people dead or missing. Her name was on the passenger list, and she was not among the living, so as far as the authorities were concerned, she had drowned. Her family identified one of the badly-decayed bodies as hers, and buried it. That, they thought, was that. However, el-Sayed had been delayed on the day of the sailing and had never made it to the ship. The Egyptian government was unimpressed: they refused to believe she was alive, and she had to go to court to prove she was not dead. In the meantime, she could not collect government benefits or work.

IN JANUARY 1985, two-year-old Michael Troche wandered out of his parents' Milwaukee home while his parents slept. The temperature had plunged to 60 degrees below zero and he soon collapsed in the snow. When his parents found him, he was frozen stiff; ice crystals had formed on and beneath his skin, and he was not breathing. He was rushed to the city's Children's Hospital, where a team of doctors and nurses worked on him for six hours. One report said that the doctors actually heard the ice crystals in his body cracking as they lifted him onto the operating table. Drugs were used to prevent his brain from swelling as he thawed, and incisions were made in his flesh to allow the tissues to expand. He remained semi-conscious for three days, and then made a rapid recovery. The doctors attributed his almost complete recovery to the wind-chill factor, which effectively quick-froze him so that his metabolism had little need for oxygen.

ANN GREEN was tried in 1650 for the murder of her illegitimate child and sentenced to be hanged. She hanged for half an hour; friends pulled her legs to help her on her way and she was beaten with a musket butt. She was cut down and taken to a house to be dissected, with the rope still tight about her neck. When her chest moved, a Mr Mason stamped upon her chest and a soldier struck her again with a musket. When the doctors came to prepare the body for dissection, she breathed. Within 14 hours, she was speaking, and the next day she prayed "very heartily". She was pardoned and later found not guilty of infanticide. She eventually died in 1659.

IN BELGIUM, a cardiologist who collapsed and died of a heart attack during a golf tournament did not let that stand in the way of winning. Pedro Brugada, a renowned heart surgeon, fell face down after hitting the ball. His heart stopped, despite the efforts of his opponent, an anæsthetist. He was rushed to hospital, where they got his heart beating again, and an hour later he was well enough to return to the tournament, which he went on to win.

THE MEDICAL DEFENCE UNION was faced with a poser by a member. One of his patients wanted to make certain that he did not come back from the dead. The elderly man disconcerted his doctor by asking that he should drive a metal stake through his heart, so he sought advice from the Union lawyers, who concluded that he was under no obligation to comply. "The same fear of entombment is more commonly expressed by patients who ask the attending doctor to open one or more veins after death so that the corpse will exsanguinate rather than revive after burial," they added in their annual report. They also suggested that in such cases, doctors should suggest a post mortem, which would cut out any possibility of being buried alive.

A YEAR after his parents thought Valentin Stoian, 12, had drowned in the Danube, and seven weeks after they had identified what they thought was his body, an aunt found the boy munching grapes in the family vineyard near Bucharest, Romania. The dead child was thought to be an unknown Bulgarian.

THE *Evenimentul Zilei* also carried the story of Nicu Mihaila, 50, from Braila in Romania who went travelling for a couple of weeks without telling friends or family. Shortly afterwards his brother Constanta Neagu, his former wife and other relatives identified a body in the local morgue as his on the basis of its clothes and stature. The corpse was buried that afternoon. At midnight Nicu arrived home to find his house sealed and knocked at the dor of his neighbour Aurica Zamfir, who fainted at the sight of him. When he got into his house he found that his relatives, with unseemly haste, had sold all his clothes.

ABRAHAM IBRAHIM AWADH'S family was in tears at his funeral, until the 'dead' sailor walked in to the tent in the Egyptian port of Alexandria where an imam was reciting funerary prayers. Hours earlier, the family had attended the burial of a man in his 30s, washed up on the Mediterranean coast, whem they thought was Awadh. Awadh explained that his wallet and identity card had been stolen. They had been found in the pocket of the corpse. The police had to exhume the body and try to find its true identity.

CHAPTER SIXTEEN

STRANGE SYNDROMES

All sorts of unusual quirks of the human body exist,
causing a surprising and surreal selection of outcomes

ROBERT MAXWELL'S mysterious demise at sea led to a re-awakening of interest in *calenture,* a strange and oddly poetic hallucinatory disorder once said to plague Spanish sailors. Dictionaries define it as a mild fever of tropical climates which impels sailors to jump into the sea. Survivors reported experiencing intense visual hallucinations which made the sea appear to be lush green fields. A 1983 study by Dr A D Macleod in the *British Journal of Medical Psychology* found that half the crew of a ship sailing from New Zealand to the UK had experienced it to some degree, showing it is still common though rarely reported. None of them had been feverish or in ill-health at the time of the experience. He believed calenture could account for many of the cases of sailors reported 'missing at sea'.

HANNAH THOMPSON, from Portsmouth, Hampshire, had all her teeth removed to prevent her biting off bits of her own body. The two-year-old suffers from sensory neuropathy type four, a hereditary genetic disorder affecting only 30 other people in the world. She has no nerve endings and cannot feel heat, cold or pain. When she sucked her thumb or chewed her fingers, she went through to the bone. She had already gnawed the ends off her fingers, damaged her arm, and bitten her tongue in half, which affected her speech. It was hoped that by the time her adult teeth came through at about the age of six, Hannah would be able to understand that she should not bite herself.

THERE HAVE BEEN fewer than 150 victims of Cockayne's Syndrome, which results in premature ageing and slow death, since its discovery by British doctor E A Cockayne in 1936. Six of the 11 children from the village of San Martin Toxpalan in central Mexico who suffer from the syndrome arrived for treatment in the city of Puebla on 22 May, 1996. They were first cousins from a family which had intermarried for three generations. Their skin was wrinkled, they were retarded, and their hearing and sight, bones and muscles were those of the very old. "Fidelia, who is 23, has the physical and biological appearance of someone aged between 90 and 100," endocrinologist Margarita Barrientos said. Blind, decrepit Fidelia arrived at the hospital in the arms of her mother – who is unaffected by the condition – together with Flavia, 19; Hilario, 16; Roberto, five; and Eduardo, two. The two young women had shown hormonal changes associated with menopause from the age of adolescence.

A MYSTERY AILMENT causing students to hallucinate, shout, wail and hurt themselves affected several schools in the Ghanaian town of Tamale. The Tamale Business Secondary School was temporarily closed after 27 of its 1,000 students fell victim to the condition which 'experts' said might be caused by drugs such as marijuana and cola nuts.

ABYS DEJESUS, a two-year-old girl from Puerto Rico, suffers from congenital hairy nevus, once known as 'human werewolf syndrome', a potentially fatal condition. She has dense brown hair over her nose and half her face, and 23 smaller patches of fur on her body. She mostly lives indoors, sheltered from other children who often run in fear from her. No-one else in her family has the condition. The condition is similar to, but apparently unrelated to, the 'werewolf gene' which affects males in a single Mexican family. Dr Adrian Lo, of St Christopher's Hospital in Philadelphia, began a three-month procedure on 27 August 1996 which he hoped would remove the hair by inflating the unblemished skin and grafting it over the surgically cleaned area. The result was expected to be much smoother and more natural than a traditional skin graft, which can leave puckers.

CHARLES BONNET was a Swiss naturalist and philosopher who described the strange hallucinations seen by his grandfather Charles Lullin, who had cataracts, in 1760. Charles Bonnet's syndrome leaves 'sane' people seeing ghosts and angels, doctors from the University Hospital in Nijmegan, Holland, reported in the *Lancet* in March 1996. Patients variously reported seeing floating figures, dragons, people wearing big flowers on their heads, and shining angels. The research showed that the condition was widespread in elderly people with bad eyesight. About one in five sufferers said they had been deceived for a short period by the hallucinations. "Often the content of the hallucinations was mundane (an unfamiliar person, a bottle, a hat), but it could be funny (two miniature policemen guiding a midget villain to a tiny prison van)," they said. Three-quarters of the patients with the syndrome had not mentioned their experiences to doctors because they did not want to be thought insane. Probably because of this, the syndrome was thought to be a rarity. Then, in 1989, a study of 500 patients with forms of visual impairment turned up 60 new cases.

ISABELLA CEOLE died of heart failure on 17 March at the age of 28. She had the body of a centenarian. She suffered from the incurable genetic condition called progeria; but rather than hide away in her home in Bologna, Italy, she went to university, regularly danced till the early hours at discos and night clubs with her friends, and worked with the disabled and AIDS patients. There are two forms of progeria, both extremely rare. One manifests in children aged about four, who seldom survive their teenage years; the other starts in adolescence and follows the same rapid progression.

THEORIES about the acquisition of language may have to be revised after the strange case of a nine-year-old boy who only learnt to speak when half his brain was removed. The boy, known only as Alex, was born with the rare Sturge–Weber syndrome, which caused him to suffer epileptic seizures untreatable with drugs. He could utter one word – 'Mama' – and one or two vowel sounds. Surgeons decided the fits could only be controlled by removing the left hemisphere of the boy's brain, a procedure carried out on about 10 patients a year. Children treated in this way can lead a nearly normal life, but have lower than average intelligence. Almost immediately after the operation, Alex's seizures disappeared and after four months, he began to speak. He is now an articulate 15-year-old and his progress is being followed by researchers from the Wolfson Institute of Child Health in London. His case caused a stir among child psychologists; since the training of Victor, 'the wild boy of Aveyron' found in the 1790s, the orthodox view is that articulate speech cannot be learnt after the age of five or six.

IN 1996, Anne Bristow-Kitney, 43, a senior producer at the BBC, suffered a cerebral hæmorrhage. When she regained consciousness, she spoke French with such a good accent that the hospital staff thought she was French. "I knew the language previously, but suddenly I was speaking it like a native," she said. "I wasn't aware of speaking French, just of communicating. I was demanding odd things too, such as 'Six glasses of wine, now!'" Further tests revealed that Anne had an aneurysm, a weak spot in one of the main arteries to the brain. The operation to clip it was a success, but six days later she had a stroke, was unable to walk and couldn't speak for some days. "Soon after, I started speaking with a Scottish accent. Some people thought it might be a relative trying to speak through me. My great-grandfather was Scottish, but I never met him. I was born in Chelsea, west London, brought up in Cheltenham, Gloucestershire, and woke up talking like an extra from *Dr Finlay's Casebook*! The doctor's explanation was that I must have met a Scot once and my brain has just picked up on it for some reason," she said. There are perhaps no more than 50 cases of Foreign Accent Syndrome described in medical literature. "It's to do with the left side of the brain that controls our ability to talk," said consultant neurosurgeon Ian Pople, of Frenchay Hospital in Bristol. "The speech control centre is left intact, but the part which links up to it is damaged, so you get a re-emergence of a first language or maybe simply a memory, as in Anne's case. It could have been someone she met only once. It's organic brain damage, as opposed to psychiatric, and is usually due to a loss of blood supply, as in a stroke, trauma, or accident. It generally gets better in time." The latest example of Foreign Accent Syndrome was reported in May, 1997. Stewart Rayner, 34, a policeman with a Cockney accent from Chingford, east London, fractured his skull in a smash at Brands Hatch, Kent. When he awoke at the Royal London Hospital, in Whitechapel, he had a deep Southern US drawl. He planned to return to work at Ilford police station in July. One of the oddest cases concerned a Norwegian woman hit on the head with shrapnel during a German air raid on her village during World War II. She fell into a coma and woke up with a German accent.

A MAN who has suffered total memory loss while he makes love is puzzling neurologists. The 64-year-old engineer would repeatedly ask his wife "What are we doing?", "What time of year is it?" and "What time of day is it?" The coital amnesia lasts 30–60 minutes, and is followed by complete recovery, though he cannot remember having had intercourse and has only a very sketchy memory of any foreplay. At no time was he unable to recognise his wife, although other sufferers from the condition have forgotten their lovers' names in the heat of passion. Dr Russell Lane, of the Neurosciences Centre at Charing Cross, west London, outlining the case in the medical journal *Neurology, Neurosurgery and Psychiatry,* said that sudden bouts of amnesia during periods of physical and emotional stress, including sex, were not uncommon. The condition is known as transient global amnesia, or TGA, and can be triggered variously by a shortage of blood in the brain, a blood clot in the brain, a form of epilepsy or migraine. The man in question was perfectly normal except for an irregular brain signal attributed to migraine, from which he had suffered for years. His loss of memory did not occur every time he had intercourse, but had happened five times in the last 18 years.

WILD TALENTS

Humans have a wide range of natural abilities – many more it seems than are usually recognised

THE HUMAN BRAIN can detect pre-earthquake tremors before seismologists. Radiographers at a hospital in Newcastle, New South Wales, found that corrupted images shown on a computer-aided tomography scan of a psychiatric patient, taken 17 minutes before a 5.5R quake struck the city in December 1989, were caused by a pre-earthquake tremor undetected by seismologists. The quake struck at 10.28am, killing 12 people and injuring hundreds. Mike Grayson, the hospital's chief radiographer, conducted the scan between 10.00am and 10.20am. He noticed the unusual streaks appearing on scans at 10.11am. The quake destroyed the scanning room, but left the patient and staff unscathed. Writing in the December issue of the *Medical Journal of Australia*, the radiographer suggested that the brain's reaction was similar to the instinct in many animals which alerts them to natural disasters before they happened. "If I ever saw that image on a screen again, I'd be the first out of the building."

A TEENAGER in the central Vietnamese province of Ninh Thuan began to glow in the dark in early 1997, according to the *Thanh Nien* newspaper. Cha Ma Le Buot, 17, first noticed in February that his body was unusually warm and covered with spots giving off a bluish-white light which flickered and died. He experiences the symptoms nightly, although by day he appears normal. He is said to be the third person to exhibit the symptoms, though many other cases appear in Christian hagiography. A fourth person turned up not far away in 1998. Truong Thi Thu Ha, 30, from a remote district in Quang Nam province, central Vietnam, discovered on 10 December that parts of her skin glowed in the dark. The glow reportedly increased when she wore nylon garments.

GOING FURTHER than just glowing, 10-year-old Liam Lowsley relished being the centre of attraction at school: blue sparks flew off his arms and legs when anyone came close to him. It had its downside. He could not operate the class computer, and the sparking sensation was unpleasant. He said: "It's worse than pins and needles." Prof Don Whitehead, head of electrical engineering at Hull University, explained that as Liam moved about, he generated huge charges of static electricity. "It is almost certainly to do with the clothes or shoes Liam wears, combined with the dry atmosphere," he said. The phenomenon only seemed to happen at Liam's school, where considered opinion related its onset to a severe thunderstorm the previous month in which the building was struck by lightning. Teacher Jonathan Roe said: "We think the scaffolding around the school may be acting as a conductor," not that that actually explained anything.

ONE TO STRAIN THE BOGGLE FACTOR: Lucy Benawell, 28, a secretary from Philadelphia, makes glass break when she stands near it for more than a minute. Unnamed doctors blame "an unusual electric charge in her body."

FORMER CRANE DRIVER Mrs Yuliya Vorobyeva, of Donetsk in the Ukraine, was declared dead at the age of 37 and spent two nights in a mortuary after receiving a 380 volt electric shock. She only revived when a doctor and his assistant began their autopsy; after that, she did not sleep for six months. When she woke up from her first long sleep, she had developed strange powers. She could see through people "as if they were a picture on a television screen," she could detect ultraviolet rays from the sun, and she could predict storms. She could also diagnose illnesses and correctly told the *Izvestia* reporter that a red liquid in his stomach indicated that he had 'had kisel', a red jelly. In the US, Greta Alexander from Illinois, who died aged 66, claimed a lightning strike gave her psychic powers. She gained national attention for helping police find missing people and bodies. She said she could visualise the past, see the future, and describe events happening 100 miles away.

AN ACADEMIC from London in her 40s, blind from birth, had an uncanny ability – similar to a bat's radar – to detect physical objects. On her way to work, she would 'count off' the lamp posts until she knew she had arrived at her office. One morning this extrasensory ability deserted her. Realising something was wrong, she consulted a neurosurgeon, who found a small meningioma in the frontal lobe of her brain. This was removed, and she is now back counting lamp posts. This may also be how an unnamed 10-year-old Japanese girl goes about carrying out her amazing feats. She can cycle down busy streets and catch balls with her eyes shut, but she can also read newspapers this way, which can't be accounted for by a form of echolocation.

A 55-YEAR-OLD Vietnamese woman, Thi Le Hang, of Ho Chi Minh Ville, has been awake since her last son was born in 1965. "In the maternity ward," she said, "leper women were also waiting to have babies. I was terrified that they might touch me and infect me with leprosy while I slept; so I deliberately stayed awake. I've never slept since." Specialists from all over the world examined her and agreed that her complaint was genuine: she appeared to suffer from a unique form of chronic post-natal shock, but claimed to feel well. "I do my gym every morning and I never feel tired," she said. "The housework doesn't bother me, but I'd really like to get a good night's sleep." At one time she was put on heavy doses of sleeping drugs and after a few weeks she appeared to doze off for a few seconds – but didn't really fall asleep. Acupuncture and magic potions of red beans also proved ineffective.

IN 1884, a bizarre case was reported from Egypt, Pennsylvania. There, an eight-year-old boy appeared to die and rise again every day. During daylight hours he seemed to be completely normal, but at dusk he collapsed into a death-like trance and remained there until morning. The strange affliction began shortly after the boy recovered from a severe bout of whooping cough. Doctors examining him were utterly confused. One reported: "I pricked him with a pin and applied a galvanic battery to his most sensitive parts (!) without creating the least impression. I forcibly raised one of his arms and it remained in an upright position. The members were like wax and were covered with indentations which I made with my fingers." He was sent to New York to be examined by 'eminent physicians'.

DOCTORS examined a six-year-old girl called Shazia, whose eyes changed colour according to the dress she wore – blue, red, yellow etc. People flocked to the girl's house in Galiyana village in the Gujrat district of Pakistan to witness the miracle.

BHANUDAS MARUTI GAIKWAD, from Marathi in India, has a form of Midas touch – instead of turning to gold, everything he touches becomes sweet, a talent he has even proved to the Rationalist Society in Pune. They washed his hands in ether, but he still went on to render buttons and other objects he touched sweet. "One day, after working in the fields, I was sleeping beneath the *audhambar* tree. Suddenly I had a dream where I saw a white flower. After which someone asked me to wake up. I looked round but saw no-one," explained Gaikwad. "Since then, whatever I have touched has tasted sweet... even my sweat is sweet."

MOHAMMED ALI MAASOOMI, 67, a farmer from Bojnoord, did not feel extremes of heat and cold. He slept naked in snow every day for two hours. He answered the door to the journalist from the *Hamshahri* newspaper in summer clothes, even though it was seven degrees below freezing. He travelled to Mecca and thought nothing of walking and praying in the blazing sun of 50 degrees C. Maasoomi noticed his strange immunity when he was 10. "I can adjust my body temperature," he said. "I inherited the ability from my father and now my son has inherited it from me."

VICKY WILLMORE, 10, from Gorton, Manchester, started writing in mirror image – with letters and numbers upside down or back to front – on 12 October 1994 after complaining of a headache. Although she could read what she wrote, nobody else could. She suffered classroom gibes and cried with frustration. Various experts examined her, but none could make a diagnosis. As the disorder became more severe and her writing degenerated into lines and squiggles, Vicky found that one of her few pleasures was following on TV the fortunes of her favourite football team, Manchester United. When they played Rotor Volgograd in the UEFA Cup on 27 September 1995, she became so excited that she jumped out of her seat and fell back, banging her head on a coffee table. The next day, Vicky, who also has a history of eyesight problems, could read and write properly again. Dr Isabella Tweedle, senior clinical medical officer for child health with the Mancunian Community Health Trust, described Vicky's cure as incredible. She said: "I have never come across anything like it before, and neither has anyone that I know of."

'PM', a 25-year-old geology student, had a fist-sized tumour removed from the right side of his brain; the operation left him epileptic and partially paralysed, but Dr P Tosca, of the University of Pavia's department of neurology noticed that PM could read and speak backwards. His first word after the operation was 'artsenif' (the Italian for window is *finestra*). The paper in the Belgian journal *Acta Neurologica Belgica* in October 1986 recalls the hypothesis that the brain stores visual images and other information in one hemisphere and mirror images on the other. It is suggested that the operation somehow liberated the mirror images stored in the non-dominant hemisphere.

REFERENCES

REFERENCES

LITTLE BIG

Giant baby: [AP] 13 Aug; NY Post, 13 Aug; NY Daily News, 13+14 Aug 1996. More big'uns: Eve. Standard (London), 4 Mar; D.Telegraph, D.Mail, Times, 5 Mar; D.Mirror, 5+10 Mar; Express, 15 Mar 1998. Strong Tom: S.Mirror, 14 Dec 1997. Mercury miniatures: [R] 27 Jan 1997. Gul Mohammed: Times, Mirror, 3 Oct; Wilmington (DE) New Journal, Delaware State News, 26 July 1997. Tall guys: Guardian, 1 Dec; Times, 10 Dec 1997; [AP], Eve. Standard (London), 3 July; Guardian, Times, Mirror, Sun, 4 July 1998. More tall ones: [AFP] 31 July 1998; Scotland on Sunday, 21 Feb 1999. Blubbery bloke: NY Post, 18+21 May; D.Telegraph, 18 May; NY Times, Victoria (BC) Times-Colonist, 19 May 1996. Big cyst: [AP] 22 Feb 1996.

BIRTHS

Unlikely: D.Telegraph, 18 June 1996. Black & white: Times, Glasgow Herald, Wolverhampton Express & Star, 10 July 1996; Dominion (Wellington, NZ), 7 Dec 1993. Noisy fœtus: Hong Kong Standard, 2 Nov 1995. Cuba kid: Western Daily Press, D.Mirror, 4 Mar 1996. Liver Salt surprise: West Briton, 25 April 1996. Mums & Mummies: [R], O Estado de São Paulo (Brazil), 3 April; [R] 3 Oct 1996. Afterbirth feast: Guardian, 17 Oct 1996. Mine's a triple: D.Mail, 6 Mar 1997. Synchronised sprogging: Times, Edinburgh Eve. News, 15 Jan 1998. Lots of 'em: S.Telegraph, 12 April 1998. Lots more: [AP] 17+26 Jan, 18 Feb, 2 Mar; S.Telegraph, 19 April 1998. Six of 'em!: Times (Malta), 13 Feb; [R] 2 Mar 1998. Record breakers: [R, AFP] 8 Aug 1998. Late payment: Irish Times, 24 June 1997.

CURIOUS CURES

One in the eye: Wolverhampton Express & Star, 17 May 1995; Southern Daily Echo, 17 Aug; S.Mirror, 14 Feb 1993. More odd blindness cures: News of the World, 18 Aug 1996, Sun, 15 Feb 1992, Melbourne Age, 23 Aug 1979; S.Mail, 28 May 1995. Bacon bot-ty: D.Mirror, 13+14 Nov; D.Record, 13 Nov 1996. Fish cure: [AP, R] 9 June 1997. Zapped acne: Edinburgh Eve. News,

Examiner (Cork), 31 July 1997. Drowning cure: *People*, 15 June 1997. Stammer swiped: *Sun*, 29 Sept 1997. Likely story: *[R]* 29 Oct; *Wolv. Express & Star*, 30 Oct 1997. Lucky accident: *[AP]* 15 Aug 1997. Worm-eye: *D. Express*, 8 Dec 1995. Magnetic fix: *[R]* 25 July 1996. Potato power: *New Scientist*, 6 June 1992. Crab crap cure: *S. Telegraph*, 4 Feb; *D.Mail*, 22 Jan 1996. Mysterious mercury poisonings: *Express on Sunday*, 14 Sept; *Times*, *D.Telegraph*, 26 Sept 1998.

MEDICAL DEVELOPMENTS

No fear: *Nature*, January; *Times*, *D.Telegraph*, 17 Jan; *NY Times*, 21 Jan; *The Week*, 25 Jan 1997. Cryptoanatomy: *Int. Herald Tribune*, 15 Feb; *New Scientist*, 24 Feb; *BMJ*, 2 Mar 1996. Ear we grow: *Independent*, 20 Dec 1996. Dream quest: *Michel Jouvet & Monique Gessain, Le Grenier des Rêves (Paris, 1997)*. Infraghost: *S.Telegraph*, 28 July; *D.Mail*, 29 July 1998. Growing condoms: *[AFP]* 12 June 1998. Shrinking brains: *D.Telegraph*, 23 Oct 1997. Grow your own: *Times*, 5 Jan 1998. Zapped walkers: *Independent*, *D.Mail*, *Guardian*, 12 June 1998. Hockey horror: *NY Times*, 17 June 1998.Taking the plunge: *Independent*, 11 May 1994. Swan pecked: *Western Morning News*, 1 Aug 1997.

EXTRA! EXTRA! READ ALL ABOUT IT

Gill people: *Cork Examiner*, 27 Jul 1996. Extra digits: *Sun*, 7 Mar, *D.Telegraph*, *Guardian*, 4 Mar 1997. Finger clan: *S.China Morning Post*, 21 Sept 1998. Born with a tail: *D.Telegraph*, 28 Nov 1988. Three eyes: *Deutsche Presse-Agentur*, 10 Feb 1997. Forked tongues: *[R, AFP]* 8 Mar 1998. Three-footer: *Aberdeen Eve. Express*, 13 May; *Times*, 14 May 1999; Three feet: *Hong Kong Standard*, 26 Mar 1998. Extra female bits: *S.China Morning Post*, 1 Aug 1997. Two todgers: *D.Record*, 24 May; *S.Express*, 26 May 1996. Twin inside: *Guardian*, *Independent*, *Times*, 3 Jul 1997. Wrong way round: *[AFP]* 2 Oct 1997; *Sun*, 5 Sept 1991. Two header: *[AFP]* 26 June; *[R]* 3 Jul; *Middlesbrough Eve.Gazette*, 20 Jul 1998. Two Brainer: *[R]*, 14 Oct 1996;

Another two header: *D.Mirror*, 23 June 1988. *[R], Jakarta (Indonesia) Post*, 5 Jan 1999. Extra gnashers: *D.Star*, 18 Oct 1991; *D.Mirror*, 3 Oct 1991, 11 Jan 1993, *[AP]* 9 Mar 1995, *Ormskirk Advertiser*, 21 Mar 1996 *Bristol Eve.Post*, 27 Dec; *D.Mail, D.Telegraph*, 29 Dec 1997, *Gould & Pyle: Anomalies and Curiosities of Medicine (1896)*. Extra breasts: *Independent*, 12 June 1992.

INEXPLICABLE!

Fuming father: *[R, AP]* 27 Apr 1994. Fumigant fella: *[AFP]* 6 Nov; *Sydney Morning Herald, Herald Sun (Melbourne)*, 7 Nov 1998. Smelly bloke: *S.Telegraph*, 10 Nov 1996. Plague mimic: *Times*, 11 Nov 1994. Wailing plague: *[R]* 27 June 1996. Laughing plague: *Bristol Eve. Post*, ? May 1996. Strange sutures: *Brisbane S.Mail*, 19 Nov 1995. Horny old woman: *Hong Kong Standard*, 16 Oct 1996. Sleeping Beauty: *Mirror*, 25 Nov; *D.Telegraph*, 26 Nov 1998. Imagined allergy: *Russel, M et al (1984) 'Learned Histamine Response' Science* **225**:*733*. Songs in the head: *[AP], Eve. Standard (London), Duluth (MN) News-Tribune & Herald*, 5 Sept 1985. Mozart medicine: *Independent*, 14 Oct 1993; *D.Telegraph*, 7 July 1992.

ODD INJURIES, STRANGE SYMPTOMS

Shampooed to death: *[AP]* 2 June 1998. Strange strike: *S.Telegraph*, 3 Sept 1995; *Times*, 12 Feb; *Independent, Guardian, D.Telegraph*, 4 July 1996. No brainer: *Salt Lake (UT) Tribune*, 18 June 1998. Flash driver: *[AP]* 30 July 1998. Bite budget: *Halifax Eve. Courier*, 1 July 1998. *Gouger Salt Lake (UT) Tribune*, 24 Nov 1998. Radiohead: *Hong Kong Standard*, 5 Oct 1997. Hiccup horror: *D.Mail, Sun*, 10 Mar 1998. Stick it where the sun don't shine: *Journal of the Royal College of Surgeons*, October 1996. Squid spikes: *Otolaryngology*,**59**, p.245, via *New Scientist*, 16 Jan 1999.

THINGS INSIDE

Bosom serpents: *D Star*, 28 June 1979; *UPI/D.Telegraph*, 12 Mar 1982. Eye bean: *Scottish Sunday Post*, 23 July 1989. Moving bullet: *D.Telegraph*, 30 December 1988; *D.Mail*, 3 Jan 1989; *Toronto Star*, 23 June 1981. Unnoticed shootings: *Leicester Mercury*, 24 May 1995; *[AFP]* 9 Aug 1997. Heavily armed: *Atlanta Constitution*, 15 Mar 1990. Ear ticket: *Bradford Argus*, 18 Feb 1987; *Sun*, 6 Aug 1994; *Disability Now*, Mar 1995. Pork boner: *National Enquirer*, 13 Feb 1990. Lung teeth: *D.Star*, 15 Sept 1995. Lung sprout: *[AP]* 15 Dec 1995. Three-penny spit: *USA Today, D Telegraph, Guardian, D.Express, Scotsman*, 21 Dec 1984; *D.Mail*, 22 Dec 1984. Rings inside: *D.Record*, 1 Feb 1994; *S.Mail (Scotland)*, 11 July 1993. Gut glass: *D.Mail*, 16 Dec 1996. Hair Gut: *D.Star*, 14 May 1991. Finger hair: *Eve.Post*, 7 Jan 1998. Hairballs: *S.Mail (Scotland)*; 8 Sept 1996, 4 Oct 1998. Nose pin: *D.Mail*, 1 Jan 1973. Rosary jam: *Source Unknown*, March 1990. Vampires live!: *Independent*, 20 Feb 1990. Fly guy: *Science*, 4 June 1954. Fly eye: *Independent on Sunday*, 15 May 1995. Bug eared: *Journal of the Royal Society of Medicine*, Jan 1998.

ODD MEDICINES

Muti-lation: *[R]*, *D.Telegraph*, 24 June 1998. Celestial cure: *S.Times*, 26 Oct 1997. Fœtus eaters: *Brisbane Courier-Mail*, 13 Apr 1995. Mole rats: *D.Mail*, 5 Jan 1998; *D.Telegraph*, 13 July 1998; *Western Mail*, 26 Aug 1995. Tiger residue: *Washington Times*, 11 Feb 1992. Things go better with coke: *Edinburgh Eve. News*, 23 Oct 1997. Smoking's good for you: *D.Record*, 21 July 1998. Ant-iseptic: *(Penang) Star*, 13 Feb 1981. Snakes alive: *Eve. Standard*, 20 Sept 1985. Special spring: *Victoria (BC) Times-Colonist*, 21 June 1997. Geophagy: *New Scientist*, 18 Oct 1997. Pile it on: *D.Telegraph*, 22 Dec 1997. Dog tonic: *D.Mirror*, 18 Aug 1995. Marmite makes it grow: *D.Mail*, 27 Mar 1995. Guinness is good for you!: *The Monitor (Uganda)*, 13–15 Sept 1995. Cabbage cure: *S.Mail*, 12 May 1991.

UNBELIEVABLE!

Talking cure: *D. Telegraph, Wolverhampton Express & Star, Independent*, 19 Dec 1997. Miracle child: *S.Express*, 16 Nov 1997. Dead miracle child: *Guernsey Eve. Press*, 5 Dec; *S.Express*, 7 Dec 1997. Lourdes miracle: *D.Mail, Mirror*, 30 Dec 1997. Lourdes lurgie: *D.Record*, 5 Nov 1993. Goretti: *D.Mail*, 28 Nov 1997. Humane horse: *People*, 4 Jul 1993. Magic Mackerel: *Celebrity*, 3–9 March 1988; *S.Mail*, 11 Dec 1997. Christmas tree cure: *Lincoln Journal*, 17 Dec 1981. Billy Ray Cyrus – miracle man!: *D.Record*, 23 Jan 1993. Miracle of Naples: *Times of Malta*, 31 Jul 1996. Sprouting finger: *S.Telegraph, S.Mirror*, 8 April 1990; *D.Record*, 9 April 1990. Statue stunner: *News of the World*, 15 Feb 1998; Coma bloke: *S.Mirror*, 30 May 1999. Proven lunacy: *Independent Magazine*, 3 Dec 1991. Alert monk: *D.Record*, 1 Aug 1992.

MEDICAL MISCELLANY

Beatles disease: *Wall Street Journal*, 24 Feb 1993. Name game: *Science Frontiers via New Scientist*, 8 Aug 1998. Fortunate flight: *D.Telegraph*, 5 May 1998. Reciprocal aid: *Times*, 18 Mar 1998. New age crazies: *Therapy Weekly*, 21 Nov 1996. IgNobility: *Times, D Telegraph*, 10 Oct 1997. Gordon Bennett!: *D.Telegraph*, 26 April 1990. Egg-straordinary aphrodisiacs: *D.Record*, 18 Aug 1995. Naked medics: *S.Mirror*, 18 Jan 1987. Exploding gut gas: *Independent*, 17 Jan 1989. Psoriasis explosion: *Edinburgh Eve.News*, 26 May 1994. Orange tan: *D.Mirror*, 1 Aug 1986. Smelly mosquito attractors: *Coventry Eve.Telegraph*, 2 Nov 1995. Gassed parrot: *Santa Monica Evening Outlook via National Lampoon*, Dec 1972. I'm walking backwards to Indonesia: *S.Mail*, 10 Sept 1995. Laotian trauma: *D.Telegraph*, 28 Dec 1990. Saw foot: *D.Mirror*, 6 Jun 1988. Tooth trauma: *Independent*, 24 Jan 1998. Long dreaming: *San José Mercury News*, 8 Apr 1995.

IT'S A COCK-UP

Scanner jam: *[AFP]* 10 Oct 1998. Dodgy docs: *Times (of Malta)*, 29 Dec 1996; *D.Telegraph*, 31 Jan 1997. Swindling psychiatrist: *Austin (TX)*

American Statesman, 12 Feb 1997. Bits inside: *Guardian*, 16 July; *South China Morning Post*, 19 Mar; *Independent*, 13 June; *[R]* 31 May 1997. Swallowed screwdriver: *The Times (of Malta)*, 6 Aug 1997. Not dead yet: *[AP,AFP]* 15 July 1997. Moonlight drive: *Sun*, 23 Jun 1993. Harley horror: *Aberdeen Eve.Express*, 24 Sept 1997. Ungrateful doc: *[R]* 19 Feb 1998. Organ takeaway: *[AP]* 30 Jan 1998. Double jeopardy: *Eastern Eve.News*, 11 April 1996. Burnt bum: *D.Telegraph*, 30 Nov 1995. Sperm scam: *M'boro Eve.Gazette*, 5 Mar 1992. Doll parts: *Rockland (NY) Journal News*, 15 Feb 1996. Not a brain surgeon: *North Bay Nugget (Ontario)*, 27 Mar 1998, *Eve. Standard (London)*, 10 Jan 1991; *LA Times*, 27 Nov 1994. Daffodil daftness: *M'boro Eve.Gazette*, 2 Mar 1994. Take that biohazard home: *[R]* 8 Sept 1997.

WEDDING TACKLE

Dicks nicked: *[R]* 2 Aug; *[AP]* 5 Aug 1997. Dick nicked con: *Focus, via Guardian*, 27 May; *S.Telegraph*, 15 June 1997. Swopsies: *Sun*, 15 Jul 1987; *Brisbane Courier Mail*, 5 Nov 1998; *D.Record*, 19 Apr 1995; *D.Star*, 11 Mar 1993. Building extensions: *Sussex Eve.Argus*, 22 Jul 1993; *Eve. Standard (London)*, 26 Nov 1997. Mechanical manhood: *Guardian*, 31 March 1998; *Sussex Eve.Argus*, 21 Aug 1995. Measuring up: *New Scientist*, 6 May 1995; *D.Mirror*, 17 March 1994; *D.Mail*, 22 Dec 1997. Foreskin farming: *Newcastle Herald*, 25 Mar 1995. Hands, feet and penises: *Express*, 6 Nov 1997. Bean there, done that: *D.Mirror, Sun*, 27 Dec 1990. Porked: *S.Mail*, 9 Nov 1997. Hot rod: *S Mirror*, 19 Apr 1998. Big stiffy: *S.China Morning Post*, 16 Jul 1997; *New Scientist*, 3 Jul 1993. Snap!: *Sun*, 9 Oct 1997. Boner: *FHM*, Jul 1998. Chinese contraceptive: *Liverpool Echo*, 16 Mar 1998. Testicle flask: *Coventry Eve. Telegraph*, 22 Jun 1998. Killjoys: *Bangkok Post*, 24 Aug 1994.

RADICAL SURGERY

De-fused: *[R], D.Telegraph, Guardian*, 13 Sept; *D.Mail*, 23 Sept 1997. Face-off: *[AFP,R], Times*, 22 Sept; *Independent*, 23 Sept 1997. Gimme some lip:

Guardian, 11 Jul 1997. A bit nasty: *D.Telegraph, Guardian, Independent, Western Morning News*, 14 July 1998. In flight surgery: *Guardian*, 23 May; *Times*, 24 May; *[AP]* 8 Dec 1995. Tonsil snipper: *Europa Times*, Jul 1993. Repossessed teeth: *Irish Times*, 31 March 1998. Bionic grandma: *Canberra Times*, 19 Apr 1998. Handy-work: *[AP]* 31 Oct 1997. Boar graft: *Sun*, 11 Mar 1992. Heart reconstruction: *Guardian*, 2 May 1998. Chunky tumour: *Times of Oman*, 1 Oct 1994. Conversation stone: *Bangkok Post*, 20 Jul 1994.

BACK FROM THE DEAD

Surviving Swami: *Manchester Guardian, via San Francisco Chronicle*, 17 November 1977. Cataplectic: *S.Mirror*, 22 Jan 1989; *Computer Talk*, Feb 1989. Primitive reflex: *The Record (NJ)*, 3 April 1990 + 21 Feb 1992; *[AP]* 29 April 1990. Doing a runner: *D.Express, Sun*, 6 April 1989. Up with a crash: *Weekend*, 14–20 Sept 1977. Raped returnee: *[AFP]* 29 April 1992. Wrong body: *Today*, 12 Sept 1992, *D.Record*, 15 Sept 1992. Another wrong body: *D.Star*, 20 Mar 1992. Resurrection denied: *NY Post*, 20 May 1992. Corpsicle: *Detroit (MI) News, [AP]* 4 Feb; *D.Mail*, 1 March; *D.Telegraph*, 30 March 1985. Ann Green: *Caulfield, James (1812). Portraits, memoirs and characters of remarkable persons, from the Revolution in 1688 to the reign of George II*. Winner all round: *Johannesburg Star*, 13 June 1995. Staying dead: *D.Telegraph*, 1 Sept 1986.Romanian return: *[AP]*, 23 Sept 1998. Another Romanian returns: *Evenimentul Zilei*, 5 Oct 1996. Surviving sailor: *S.China Morning Post*, 13 oct 1997.

STRANGE SYNDROMES

Calenture: *Guardian*, 8 Nov 1991. Sensory neuropathy type four: *Portsmouth News*, 30 May; *D.Mirror, D.Star*, 31 May 1996. Cockayne's Syndrome: *[R]* 25 May 1996. Mystery Hysteria: *Western Morning News*, 27 June 1996. Hairy nevus: *[AP]* 27 Aug 1996. Charles Bonnet's Syndrome: *British Journal of Psychiatry* **166**:254–57, Feb 1995; *[R]* 23 Mar 1996. Progeria: *Mirror*, 20 Mar 1997. Sturge–Weber Syndrome: *D.Mail*, 30 Mar; *Independent*, 19 April

1997. Foreign Accent Syndrome: *D.Record*, 27 Mar; *D.Mail*, 22 April; *Sun*, 30 May; *Chingford Guardian*, 5+19 June 1997. Transient Global Amnesia: *D.Telegraph, D.Mail, Independent, NY Post*, 5 Aug 1997.

WILD TALENTS

Quake detector: *Times*, 28 Dec 1996. Glowing people: *[AFP]* 5 Mar 1997, *[AFP]* 24 Dec 1998. Sparky: *Sun*, 31 Mar 1995. Glass zapper: *D.Star*, 11 July 1995. Electric psychic: *Izvestia*, 14 June 1987; *[AP]* 19 July 1998. Bat people: *S.Telegraph Magazine*, 28 June 1998. Sleepless: *S.Express*, 23 Mar 1997. Constant resurrections: *London (Ontario) Free Press*, 25 Mar 1884. Colour changer: *Saudi Gazette, Arab News*, 22 Oct 1998. Sweetie *The Asian Age*, 22 Feb 1996. Strange scribbler: *Times, D.Telegraph, D.Mail*, 7 Dec; *Manchester Metro News*, 8 Dec 1995. Mirror Man: *D.Telegraph*, 23 Oct 1986.

Other books available in the *Fortean Times Book Of* Series:

STRANGE DEATHS £4.99

More than 350 exotic extinctions including: death by doughnut, flying turnip tragedy, chainsaw suicides and cactus revenge.

INEPT CRIME £4.99

More than 375 farcical felonies, including: don't hide a lobster down your underpants, chilli pepper enema, dental floss jailbreak and guard dogs stolen.

LIFE'S LOSERS £4.99

More than 400 tragic tough-luck stories, including: letter bomb returned to sender, the ear that went of, the skydiver who forgot his parachute and God gets mugged.

EXPLODING PIGS £4.99

More than 375 bizarre beast stories including iguanas at the wheel, Johnny Depp's armadillo sex attack, goldfish swallows shark and lesbian sheep.

MORE STRANGE DEATHS £4.99

More than 375 fanciful fatalities including toenail avalanche disaster, inflatable elephant horror, bat dung bombing and sky diving Elvis tragedy.

BIZARRE BEHAVIOUR £4.99

More than 375 outlandish occurrences including Santa takes hostages, dead cat mania, voodoo class control and penis shrinking panics.

To order please call **01789 490 715** or complete the form overleaf

Item	Code	UK Price	US Price	OS Price	Qty	Value
STRANGE DEATHS	FT05A	£4.99	$11.00	£5.50		
INEPT CRIME	FT71A	£4.99	$11.00	£5.50		
LIFE'S LOSERS	FT72A	£4.99	$11.00	£5.50		
EXPLODING PIGS	FT45B	£4.99	$11.00	£5.50		
MORE STRANGE DEATHS	FT79B	£4.99	$11.00	£5.50		
BIZARRE BEHAVIOUR	FT78B	£4.99	$11.00	£5.50		

Postage and packing are free   **Total £** _____

Mr/Mrs/Ms _____

Address _____

_____

_____

_____ Postcode _____

Telephone _____

☐ I enclose a cheque/International money order for £_____
made payable to **Dennis Direct**. *(If paying in dollars please make
cheques payable to John Brown Publishing)*

☐ Please debit the above amount from my (tick one)

☐ Visa   ☐ Mastercard   ☐ American Express

☐ Switch (issue no. _____)

Card No. (please fill in boxes below)

☐☐☐☐☐☐   ☐☐☐☐☐☐   ☐☐☐☐☐☐   ☐☐☐☐☐

Vaid from ☐☐ ☐☐   Expiry date ☐☐ ☐☐

Signature _____

Date _____

☐ Please tick if you would prefer not to receive occasional mailings from selected companies

Please return this order form to:
Fortean Times, PO Box 2505, Alcester, Warwickshire B50 4JU. UK
or phone charge card details on **(44) 01789 490 215.**
Allow 28 days for delivery in the UK, 6-8 weeks for overseas orders.